THE RHYMING RIVER

IV

POETRY BOOKS BY JAMES REEVES

ANTHOLOGIES

Heinemann's Junior Poetry Books: a collection of rhymes and poems
for use in primary schools
1 *Yellow Wheels*
2 *Grey Goose and Gander*
3 *Green Broom*
4 *Strawberry Fair*
The Merry-Go-Round (the above four books in one volume)
The Rhyming River: an anthology of poetry for secondary schools
Book One (illustrated by Peter Dunbar)
Book Two (illustrated by Jane Paton)
Book Three (illustrated by Robert Hodgson)
Book Four (illustrated by Peggy Fortnum)
Orpheus Book I (English poetry for 10-12-year-olds)
Orpheus Book II (English poetry for 13-15-year-olds)
The Poets' World (an anthology of English poetry)
The Speaking Oak (a miscellany of English prose and poetry)

POEMS FOR CHILDREN

Hurdy Gurdy
The Wandering Moon
Prefabulous Animiles with Edward Ardizzone

THE POETRY BOOKSHELF SERIES

Selections with introductions and notes
D. H. Lawrence
John Donne
Gerard Manley Hopkins
John Clare
Robert Browning
Samuel Taylor Coleridge
Emily Dickinson
The Modern Poets' World

THE RHYMING RIVER
BOOK IV

an anthology of verse chosen by
JAMES REEVES

with illustrations by
PEGGY FORTNUM
and from contemporary sources

HEINEMANN EDUCATIONAL
BOOKS LTD · LONDON

Heinemann Educational Books Ltd

LONDON   MELBOURNE   TORONTO
SINGAPORE   CAPE TOWN
AUCKLAND   IBADAN
HONG KONG

Published by Heinemann Educational Books Ltd
48 Charles Street, London W1
Printed in Great Britain by
Butler & Tanner Ltd
Frome and London

CONTENTS

I

II

III

V

I

Song

SHAKE off your heavy trance!
  And leap into a dance
Such as no mortals use to tread:
  Fit only for Apollo
To play to, for the moon to lead,
  And all the stars to follow!

FRANCIS BEAUMONT

Orpheus

ORPHEUS with his lute made trees,
And the mountain tops that freeze,
  Bow themselves when he did sing:
To his music plants and flowers
Ever sprung, as sun and showers
  There had made a lasting spring.

Every thing that heard him play,
Even the billows of the sea,
  Hung their heads and then lay by.
In sweet music is such art,
Killing care and grief of heart
  Fall asleep, or hearing die.

          JOHN FLETCHER

Says Tweed to Till

SAYS Tweed to Till—
'What gars[1] ye rin sae still?'
Says Till to Tweed—
'Though ye rin with speed
  And I rin slaw,
For ae man that ye droon
  I droon twa.'

   [1] Makes.

The Eddystone Light

MY father was the keeper of the Eddystone Light,
And he married a mermaid one fine night.
From this union there came three;
Two were fish and the other was me.

One night while I was a-trimming of the glim,
A-singing a verse from the evening hymn,
A voice from the starboard shouted 'Ahoy!'
And there was my mother a-sitting on a buoy.

'Oh, what has become of the children three?'
My mother then she asked of me.
'One was exhibited as a talking fish,
And the other was served in a chafing-dish.'

Then the phosphorus flashed in her seaweed hair,
I looked again and my mother wasn't there.
A voice came echoing out of the night,
'To hell with the keeper of the Eddystone Light!'

The Wind and the Rain

WHEN that I was and a little tiny boy,
  With hey, ho, the wind and the rain;
A foolish thing was but a toy,
  For the rain it raineth every day.

But when I came to man's estate,
  With hey, ho, the wind and the rain;
'Gainst knaves and thieves men shut their gate,
  For the rain it raineth every day.

But when I came, alas! to wive,
  With hey, ho, the wind and the rain;
By swaggering could I never thrive,
  For the rain it raineth every day.

But when I came unto my bed,
  With hey, ho, the wind and the rain;
With toss-pots still had drunken head,
  For the rain it raineth every day.

4

A great while ago the world begun,
  With hey, ho, the wind and the rain;
But that's all one, our play is done,
  And we'll strive to please you every day.

WILLIAM SHAKESPEARE

There'll never be Peace

By yon castle wa', at the close of the day,
I heard a man sing, tho' his head it was grey;
And as he was singing, the tears fast down came,
There'll never be peace till Jamie comes hame.

The Church is in ruins, the State is in jars,
Delusions, oppressions, and murderous wars:
We darena weel say 't, tho' we ken wha 's to blame—
There 'll never be peace till Jamie comes hame.

My seven braw sons for Jamie drew sword,
And now I greet[1] round their green beds in the yerd.
It brak the sweet heart of my faithful auld dame—
There 'll never be peace till Jamie comes hame.

Now life is a burden that bows me down,
Sin' I tint[2] my bairns, and he tint his crown;
But till my last moments my words are the same—
There 'll never be peace till Jamie comes hame.

ROBERT BURNS

[1] Weep. [2] Lost.

How Pleasant to know Mr Lear!

'How pleasant to know Mr Lear!'
　　Who has written such volumes of stuff!
Some think him ill-tempered and queer,
　　But a few think him pleasant enough.

His mind is concrete and fastidious,
　　His nose is remarkably big;
His visage is more or less hideous,
　　His beard it resembles a wig.

He has ears, and two eyes, and ten fingers,
　　Leastways if you reckon two thumbs;
Long ago he was one of the singers,
　　But now he is one of the dumbs.

He sits in a beautiful parlour,
　　With hundreds of books on the wall;
He drinks a great deal of Marsala,
　　But never gets tipsy at all.

He has many friends, laymen and clerical,
　　Old Foss is the name of his cat:
His body is perfectly spherical,
　　He weareth a runcible hat.

When he walks in a waterproof white,
　　The children run after him so!
Calling out, 'He's come out in his night-
　　gown, that crazy old Englishman, oh!'

6

He weeps by the side of the ocean,
    He weeps on the top of the hill;
He purchases pancakes and lotion,
    And chocolate shrimps from the mill.

He reads but he cannot speak Spanish,
    He cannot abide ginger-beer:
Ere the days of his pilgrimage vanish,
    How pleasant to know Mr Lear !

EDWARD LEAR

7

An Imitation of Wordsworth

HE lived amidst th' untrodden ways
 To Rydal Lake that lead;
A bard whom there were none to praise,
 And very few to read.

Behind a cloud his mystic sense,
 Deep hidden who can spy?
Bright as the night when not a star
 Is hidden in the sky.

Unread his works—his 'Milk White Doe'
 With dust is dark and dim;
It's still in Longman's shop, and oh!
 The difference to him!

HARTLEY COLERIDGE

The Artist

The Artist and his Luckless Wife
They lead a horrid haunted life,
Surrounded by the things he's made
That are not wanted by the trade.

The world is very fair to see;
The Artist will not let it be;
He fiddles with the works of God,
And makes them look uncommon odd.

The Artist is an awful man,
He does not do the things he can;
He does the things he cannot do,
And we attend the private view.

The Artist uses honest paint
To represent things as they ain't,
He then asks money for the time
It took to perpetrate the crime.

SIR WALTER RALEIGH

Poor Rumble

PITY poor Rumble: he is growing wheezy.
    At seventy-nine years old
His breath comes hard, and nothing comes too easy.
    He finds the evenings cold.

Pity poor Rumble: winter on his noddle
    Has laid its wisps of snow;
And though about the place he scarce can toddle,
    He likes to work, I know.

Pity poor Rumble: his last teeth are rotting
    Back in his square old head;
And yet, come Whitsuntide, you'll find him potting
    Down in his potting-shed.

Pity poor Rumble: since the time of Noah
    There was in all the county
For rose, or root, or greens no better grower—
    It was sheer bounty.

He was the champion for fruit or tatey;
    But Rumble's famous marrow,
So huge it was and more than common weighty,
    It almost split his barrow.

Of cat and dog he was the holy terror—
    None ever plagued him twice;
And if a slug walked on his lawn in error,
    His language was not nice.

Pity poor Rumble: now his strength is going.
    No more he'll cut up wood.
I wish I had some peaches of his growing;
    They were so very good.

Sing, birds of the air, for Martin Rumble, please.
    When he is gone away,
Who will grow strawberries for you, green peas,
    And currants on the spray?

                           JAMES REEVES

When Pat came over the Hill

AND when Pat came over the hill his colleen fair to see
His whistle low but shrill the signal was to be.
Oh May, the Mother cried, there's somebody whistling sure.
Oh Mother, it is the wind you know that's whistling through the
  door.

I've lived a long time Mary in this wide world my dear,
But the door to whistle like that I never yet did hear.
But Mother you know the fiddle hangs close beside the chink
And the wind upon the string is playing the tune I think.

The dog is barking now the fiddle can't play the tune.
But Mother you know they say dogs bark when they see the
  moon.
But how can he see the moon when he's old and blind?
Blind dogs don't bark at the moon you know nor fiddles don't
  play with the wind.

And now I hear the pig uneasy in his mind.
But Mother you know they say that pigs can see the wind.
That's true enough my dear but I think you may remark
That pigs no more than we can see anything in the dark.

I'm not such a fool as you think, I know very well it's Pat.
Go home you whistling thief and do get away out of that.
And you go into bed, don't play upon me your jeers,
For although I've lost my sight I haven't lost my ears.

And you lads when courting go and for your Sweetheart wait
Take care not to whistle too loud in case the old woman might
    wake.
From the days when I was young forget I never can
I knew the difference between a fiddle, a dog, and a man.

At the Setting of the Sun

COME all you young fellows that carry a gun,
Beware of late shooting when daylight is done,
For 'tis little you reckon what hazards you run,
I shot my true love at the setting of the sun.

In a shower of rain as my darling did hie[1]
All under the bushes to keep herself dry,
With her head in her apron I thought her a swan,
And I shot my true love at the setting of the sun.

I'll fly from my country, I nowhere find rest,
I've shot my true love like a bird in her nest.
Like lead on my heart lies the deed I have done,
I shot my true love at the setting of the sun.

In the night the fair maid as a white swan appears,
She says, O my true love, quick dry up your tears,
I freely forgive you, I have Paradise won,
I was shot by my love at the setting of the sun.

[1] Go.

13

O the years as they pass leave me lonely and sad,
I can ne'er love another and naught makes me glad.
I wait and expect till life's little span done
I meet my true love at the rising of the sun.

The 'General Elliott'

HE fell in victory's fierce pursuit,
  Holed through and through with shot.
A sabre sweep had hacked him deep
  Twixt neck and shoulder knot. . . .

The potman cannot well recall,
  The ostler never knew,
Whether his day was Malplaquet,
  The Boyne, or Waterloo.

But there he hangs for tavern sign,
  With foolish bold regard
For cock and hen and loitering men
  And wagons down the yard.

Raised high above the hayseed world
  He smokes his painted pipe,
And now surveys the orchard ways,
  The damsons clustering ripe.

He sees the churchyard slabs beyond,
  Where country neighbours lie,
Their brief renown set lowly down;
  His name assaults the sky.

He grips the tankard of brown ale
  That spills a generous foam:
Oft-times he drinks, they say, and winks
  At drunk men lurching home.

No upstart hero may usurp
  That honoured swinging seat;
His seasons pass with pipe and glass
  Until the tale's complete.

And paint shall keep his buttons bright
  Though all the world's forgot
Whether he died for England's pride
  By battle, or by pot.

ROBERT GRAVES

There is a Lady Sweet and Kind

THERE is a Lady sweet and kind,
Was never face so pleased my mind;
I did but see her passing by,
And yet I love her till I die.

Her gesture, motion and her smiles
Her wit, her voice my heart beguiles,
Beguiles my heart, I know not why,
And yet I love her till I die.

Her free behaviour, winning looks,
Will make a lawyer burn his books;
I touched her not, alas! not I,
And yet I love her till I die.

Had I her fast betwixt mine arms,
Judge you that think such sports were harms;
Weren't any harm? no, no, fie, fie,
For I will love her till I die.

Should I remain confined there
So long as Phoebus in his sphere,
I to request, she to deny,
Yet would I love her till I die.

Cupid is wingèd and doth range,
Her country so my love doth change:
But change she earth, or change she sky,
Yet will I love her till I die.

The Daniel Jazz

DARIUS the Mede was a king and a wonder.
His eye was proud, and his voice was thunder.
He kept bad lions in a monstrous den.
He fed up the lions on Christian men.

Daniel was the chief hired man of the land.
He stirred up the jazz in the palace band.
He whitewashed the cellar. He shovelled in the coal.
And Daniel kept a-praying: 'Lord, save my soul.'
Daniel kept a-praying: 'Lord, save my soul.'
Daniel kept a-praying: 'Lord, save my soul.'

Daniel was the butler, swagger and swell.
He ran upstairs. He answered the bell.
And *he* would let in whoever came a-calling:
Saints so holy, scamps so appalling.
'Old man Ahab leaves his card.
Elisha and the bears are a-waiting in the yard.
Here comes Pharaoh and his snakes a-calling.
Here comes Cain and his wife a-calling.
Shadrach, Meshach and Abednego for tea.
Here comes Jonah and the whale,
And the *Sea*!
Here comes St Peter and his fishing-pole.
Here comes Judas and his silver a-calling.
Here comes old Beelzebub a-calling.'

And Daniel kept a-praying: 'Lord, save my soul.'
Daniel kept a-praying: 'Lord, save my soul.'
Daniel kept a-praying: 'Lord, save my soul.'

His sweetheart and his mother were Christian and meek.
They washed and ironed for Darius every week.
One Thursday he met them at the door:
Paid them as usual, but acted sore.
He said: 'Your Daniel is a dead little pigeon.
He's a good hard worker, but he talks religion.'
And he showed them Daniel in the lion's cage.
Daniel standing quietly, the lions in a rage.

His good old mother cried:—
'Lord, save him.'
And Daniel's tender sweetheart cried:—
'Lord, save him.'

And she was a golden lily in the dew.
And she was as sweet as an apple on the tree.
And she was as fine as a melon in the corn-field,
Gliding and lovely as a ship on the sea,
Gliding and lovely as a ship on the sea.
And she prayed to the Lord:—
'*Send* Gabriel. *Send* Gabriel.'

King Darius said to the lions:—
'Bite Daniel. Bite Daniel.
Bite him. Bite him. Bite him!'

Thus roared the lions:—
'We want Daniel, Daniel, Daniel,
We want Daniel, Daniel, Daniel.
Grrrrrrrrrrrrrrrrrrrrrrrrrrrrrr.
Grrrrrrrrrrrrrrrrrrrrrrrrrrrrrr.'
And Daniel did not frown,
Daniel did not cry.
He kept on looking at the sky.
And the Lord said to Gabriel:—
'Go chain the lions down,
Go chain the lions down.
Go chain the lions down.
Go chain the lions down.'
And *Gabriel* chained the lions,
And Gabriel chained the lions,
And *Gabriel* chained the lions,
And Daniel got out of the den,
And Daniel got out of the den,
And Daniel got out of the den.
And Darius said: 'You're a Christian child,'
Darius said: 'You're a Christian child,'
Darius said: 'You're a Christian child,'
And gave him his job again,
And gave him his job again,
And gave him his job again.

VACHEL LINDSAY

II

That Sea-Beast Leviathan

(from *Paradise Lost*)

Him haply slumbering on the Norway foam
The pilot of some small night-foundered skiff,
Deeming some island, oft, as seamen tell,
With fixèd anchor in his scaly rind
Moors by his side under the lee, while night
Invests the sea, and wishèd morn delays.

JOHN MILTON

The Whale

To explain the nature of fishes in craft of verse—
And first, the Great Whale. A grim purpose is his;
Mariners often find him against their will
Floating on eternal ocean.
His name is Fastitocolon,
His coat is like rough stone,
Like a huge sea-knot of wrack, ringed with sand-dunes,
That floats by the shore.
    Now when wave-borne men trust their eyes for an island,
And moor their high-beaked ships to the fraudy shore,
Tether their sea-horses at the brink of ocean
And roam up the island to explore:
While the keels lie at the tide-mark
The tired sailors make their camp,
They wake a fire on the island,
Happy are the men, and tired—glad to encamp.
But he is crafty and treacherous; when he feels
The travellers properly planted and set
Taking the pretty weather—Instantly down
Darts the oceanic animal,
And locks drowning in the hall of death
Both ships and souls!

Anglo-Saxon, translated by GAVIN BONE

Leviathan

(The Creator speaks to Job)

'CANST thou draw out leviathan with an hook?
Or his tongue with a cord which thou lettest down?
Canst thou put an hook into his nose?
Or bore his jaw through with a thorn? . . .
Who can open the doors of his face?
His teeth are terrible round about.
His scales are his pride,
Shut up together as with a close seal . . .
Out of his mouth go burning lamps,
And sparks of fire leap out.
Out of his nostrils goeth smoke,
As out of a seething pot or cauldron.
His breath kindleth coals,
And a flame goeth out of his mouth . . .
He maketh the deep to boil like a pot:
He maketh the sea like a pot of ointment.
He maketh a path to shine after him;
One would think the deep to be hoary.
Upon earth there is not his like,
Who is made without fear.
He beholdeth all high things:
He is a king over all the children of pride.'

THE BOOK OF JOB

Riddle on Moon and Sun

'I SAW a creature sally with booty,
Between its horns bearing treasures amazing.
'Twas a bright cup of the air, a brave, pipkin-thing
Adorned with delicate, darting rays.
This plunder gay for a bower it would take
Spoil of the air, to its palace dim,
And, cunning, would build a room of its own in heaven.
Over the wall an arrogant being
Sprang up, though common to all men's sight is he.
He snatched the booty, drove the other home,
Wisp of a pilgrim; and westwards itself
The cruel creature went careering on.
Dust blew up. Dew came down.
The night followed after. But never a man
Knew where the wandering thing had gone.'

Anglo-Saxon, translated by GAVIN BONE

Morning Express

ALONG the wind-swept platform, pinched and white,
The travellers stand in pools of wintry light,
Offering themselves to morn's long slanting arrows.
The train's due; porters trundle laden barrows.
The train steams in, volleying resplendent clouds
Of sun-blown vapour. Hither and about,
Scared people hurry, storming the doors in crowds.
The officials seem to waken with a shout,
Resolved to hoist and plunder; some to the vans
Leap; others rumble the milk in gleaming cans.
Boys, indolent-eyed, from baskets leaning back,
Question each face; a man with a hammer steals
Stooping from coach to coach; with clang and clack
Touches and tests, and listens to the wheels.
Guard sounds a warning whistle, points to the clock
With brandished flag, and on his folded flock
Claps the last door: the monster grunts: 'Enough!'
Tightening his load of links with pant and puff.
Under the arch, then forth into blue day,
Glide the processional windows on their way,
And glimpse the stately folk who sit at ease
To view the world like kings taking the seas
In prosperous weather: drifting banners tell
Their progress to the counties; with them goes
The clamour of their journeying; while those
Who sped them stand to wave a last farewell.

SIEGFRIED SASSOON

UNITED STATES EXPRESS TRAIN, 1866
(Lithograph)

The Train

I LIKE to see it lap the miles,
And lick the valleys up,
And stop to feed itself at tanks;
And then, prodigious, step

Around a pile of mountains,
And, supercilious, peer
In shanties by the sides of roads;
And then a quarry pare

To fit its sides, and crawl between,
Complaining all the while
In horrid, hooting stanza;
Then chase itself down hill

And neigh like Boanerges:
Then, punctual as a star,
Stop—docile and omnipotent—
At its own stable door.

EMILY DICKINSON

To Mistress Margaret Hussey

MERRY Margaret,
As midsummer flower,
Gentle as falcon,
Or hawk of the tower;
With solace and gladness,
Much mirth and no madness,
All good and no badness;
So joyously,
So maidenly,
So womanly,
Her demeaning,
In every thing,
Far, far passing
That I can indite,
Or suffice to write,
Of Merry Margaret,
As midsummer flower,
Gentle as falcon,
Or hawk of the tower;
As patient and still,
And as full of good will,
As fair Isiphil,
Coliander,
Sweet pomander,
Good Cassander;

Stedfast of thought,
Well made, well wrought,
Far may be sought,
Erst that ye can find
So courteous, so kind,
As Merry Margaret,
This midsummer flower,
Gentle as falcon,
Or hawk of the tower.

JOHN SKELTON

Prelude

THE winter evening settles down
With smell of steaks in passageways.
Six o'clock.
The burnt-out ends of smoky days.
And now a gusty shower wraps
The grimy scraps
Of withered leaves about your feet
And newspapers from vacant lots;
The showers beat
On broken blinds and chimney-pots,
And at the corner of the street
A lonely cab-horse steams and stamps.
And then the lighting of the lamps.

T. S. ELIOT

An Eighteenth-Century Poor House

THEIRS is yon house that holds the Parish Poor,
Whose walls of mud scarce bear the broken door;
There, where the putrid vapours flagging, play,
And the dull wheel hums doleful through the day;—
There Children dwell who know no Parents' care;
Parents, who know no Children's love, dwell there;
Heart-broken Matrons on their joyless bed,
Forsaken Wives and Mothers never wed;
Dejected Widows with unheeded tears,
And crippled Age with more than child-hood fears;
The Lame, the Blind, and far the happiest they!
The moping Idiot and the Madman gay.

GEORGE CRABBE

The Runaway

ONCE when the snow of the year was beginning to fall,
We stopped by a mountain pasture to say, 'Whose colt?'
A little Morgan had one forefoot on the wall,
The other curled at his breast. He dipped his head
And snorted at us. And then he had to bolt.
We heard the miniature thunder where he fled,
And we saw him, or thought we saw him, dim and grey,
Like a shadow against the curtain of falling flakes.
'I think the little fellow's afraid of the snow.
He isn't winter-broken. It isn't play
With the little fellow at all. He's running away.
I doubt if even his mother could tell him, "Sakes,
It's only weather." He'd think she didn't know!
Where is his mother? He can't be out alone.'
And now he comes again with clatter of stone,
And mounts the wall again with whited eyes

And all his tail that isn't hair up straight.
He shudders his coat as if to throw off flies.
'Whoever it is that leaves him out so late,
When other creatures have gone to stall and bin,
Ought to be told to come and take him in.'

ROBERT FROST

Two Performing Elephants

HE stands with his forefeet on the drum
and the other, the old one, the pallid hoary female
must creep her great bulk beneath the bridge of him.

On her knees, in utmost caution
all agog, and curling up her trunk
she edges through without upsetting him.
Triumph! the ancient, pig-tailed monster!

When her trick is to climb over him
with what shadow-like slow carefulness
she skims him, sensitive
as shadows from the ages gone and perished
in touching him, and planting her round feet.

While the wispy, modern children, half-afraid
watch silent. The looming of the hoary, far-gone ages
is too much for them.

D. H. LAWRENCE

A Narrow Fellow in the Grass

A NARROW fellow in the grass
Occasionally rides:
You may have met him—did you not?
His notice sudden is.

The grass divides as with a comb,
A spotted shaft is seen;
And then it closes at your feet
And opens further on.

He likes a boggy acre,
A floor too cool for corn.
Yet when a child, and barefoot,
I more than once, at morn,

Have passed, I thought, a whip-lash
Unbraiding in the sun—
When, stooping to secure it,
It wrinkled, and was gone.

Several of nature's people
I know, and they know me;
I feel for them a transport
Of cordiality;

But never met this fellow,
Attended or alone,
Without a tighter breathing,
And zero at the bone.

EMILY DICKINSON

Snake

A SNAKE came to my water-trough
On a hot, hot day, and I in pyjamas for the heat,
To drink there.

In the deep, strange-scented shade of the great dark carob-tree
I came down the steps with my pitcher
And must wait, must stand and wait, for there he was at the
    trough before me.

He reached down from a fissure in the earth-wall in the gloom
And trailed his yellow-brown slackness soft-bellied down, over
    the edge of the stone trough
And rested his throat upon the stone bottom,
And where the water had dripped from the tap, in a small clear-
    ness,
He sipped with his straight mouth,
Softly drank through his straight gums, into his slack long body,
Silently.

Someone was before me at my water-trough,
And I, like a second comer, waiting.

He lifted his head from his drinking, as cattle do,
And looked at me vaguely, as drinking cattle do,
And flickered his two-forked tongue from his lips, and mused a
    moment,
And stooped and drank a little more,
Being earth-brown, earth-golden from the burning bowels of the
    earth
On the day of Sicilian July, with Etna smoking.

The voice of my education said to me
He must be killed,
For in Sicily the black, black snakes are innocent, the gold are
    venomous.

And voices in me said, If you were a man
You would take a stick and break him now, and finish him off.

But must I confess how I liked him,
How glad I was he had come like a guest in quiet, to drink at my
    water-trough
And depart peaceful, pacified, and thankless,
Into the burning bowels of this earth?

Was it cowardice, that I dared not kill him?
Was it perversity, that I longed to talk to him?
Was it humility, to feel so honoured?
I felt so honoured.

And yet those voices:
If you were not afraid, you would kill him!
And truly I was afraid, I was most afraid,
But even so, honoured still more
That he should seek my hospitality
From out the dark door of the secret earth.

He drank enough
And lifted his head, dreamily, as one who has drunken,
And flickered his tongue like a forked night on the air, so black,
Seeming to lick his lips,
And looked around like a god, unseeing, into the air,
And slowly turned his head,
And slowly, very slowly, as if thrice adream,
Proceeded to draw his slow length curving round
And climb again the broken bank of my wall-face.
And as he put his head into that dreadful hole,
And as he slowly drew up, snake-easing his shoulders, and entered farther,
A sort of horror, a sort of protest against his withdrawing into that horrid black hole,
Deliberately going into the blackness, and slowly drawing himself after,
Overcame me now his back was turned.

I looked round, I put down my pitcher,
I picked up a clumsy log
And threw it at the water-trough with a clatter.

I think it did not hit him,
But suddenly that part of him that was left behind convulsed in
    undignified haste,
Writhed like lightning, and was gone
Into the black hole, the earth-lipped fissure in the wall-front,
At which, in the intense still noon, I stared with fascination.

And immediately I regretted it.
I thought how paltry, how vulgar, what a mean act!
I despised myself and the voices of my accursed human education.

And I thought of the albatross,
And I wished he would come back, my snake.

For he seemed to me again like a king,
Like a king in exile, uncrowned in the underworld,
Now due to be crowned again.

And so I missed my chance with one of the lords
Of life.
And I have something to expiate;
A pettiness.

D. H. LAWRENCE

The Tyger

TYGER! Tyger! burning bright
In the forests of the night,
What immortal hand or eye
Could frame thy fearful symmetry?

In what distant deeps or skies
Burnt the fire of thine eyes?
On what wings dare he aspire?
What the hand dare seize the fire?

And what shoulder, and what art,
Could twist the sinews of thy heart?
And when thy heart began to beat,
What dread hand? and what dread feet?

What the hammer? what the chain?
In what furnace was thy brain?
What the anvil? what dread grasp
Dare its deadly terror clasp?

When the stars threw down their spears,
And watered heaven with their tears,
Did he smile his work to see?
Did he who made the Lamb make thee?

Tyger! Tyger! burning bright
In the forests of the night,
What immortal hand or eye
Dare frame thy fearful symmetry?

WILLIAM BLAKE

The Main-Deep

THE long-rólling,
Steady-póuring,
Deep-trenchéd
Green billów:

The wide-topped,
Unbróken,
Green-glacid,
Slow-sliding,

Cold-flushing,
—On—on—on—
Chill-rushing,
Hush-hushing,

. . . Hush-hushing . . .

JAMES STEPHENS

Patrolling Barnegat

WILD, wild the storm, and the sea high running,
Steady the roar of the gale, with incessant undertone muttering,
Shouts of demoniac laughter fitfully piercing and pealing,
Waves, air, midnight, their savagest trinity lashing,
Out in the shadows there milk-white combs careering,
On beachy slush and sand spurts of snow fierce slanting,
Where through the murk the easterly death-wind breasting,
Through cutting swirl and spray watchful and firm advancing,
(That in the distance! is that a wreck? is the red signal flaring?)
Slush and sand of the beach tireless till daylight wending,
Steadily, slowly, through hoarse roar never remitting,
Along the midnight edge by those milk-white combs careering,
A group of dim, weird forms, struggling, the night confronting,
That savage trinity warily watching.

WALT WHITMAN

VIEW OF WESTMINSTER BRIDGE, ABOUT 1800
from an engraving

Composed upon Westminster Bridge

EARTH has not any thing to show more fair:
Dull would he be of soul who could pass by
A sight so touching in its majesty.
This City now doth, like a garment, wear
The beauty of the morning; silent, bare,
Ships, towers, domes, theatres, and temples lie
Open unto the fields, and to the sky,
All bright and glittering in the smokeless air.
Never did sun more beautifully steep
In his first splendour, valley, rock, or hill;
Ne'er saw I, never felt, a calm so deep!
The river glideth at his own sweet will:
Dear God! the very houses seem asleep,
And all that mighty heart is lying still!

WILLIAM WORDSWORTH

Snow in the Suburb

EVERY branch big with it,
  Bent every twig with it;
Every fork like a white web-foot;
Every street and pavement mute:
Some flakes have lost their way, and grope back upward, when
Meeting those meandering down they turn and descend again.
  The palings are glued together like a wall,
  And there is no waft of wind with the fleecy fall.

  A sparrow enters the tree,
    Whereon immediately
  A snow-lump thrice his own slight size
  Descends on him and showers his head and eyes,
    And overturns him,
    And near inurns him,
  And lights on a nether twig, when its brush
Starts off a volley of other lodging lumps with a rush.

  The steps are a blanched slope,
    Up which, with feeble hope,
A black cat comes, wide-eyed and thin;
    And we take him in.

                                        THOMAS HARDY

43

Wiltshire Downs

THE cuckoo's double note
Loosened like bubbles from a drowning throat
Floats through the air
In mockery of pipit, lark and stare.

The stable-boys thud by
Their horses slinging divots at the sky
And with bright hooves
Printing the sodden turf with lucky grooves.

As still as a windhover
A shepherd in his flapping coat leans over
His tall sheep-crook
And shearlings, tegs and yoes cons like a book.

And one tree-crowned long barrow
Stretched like a sow that has brought forth her farrow
Hides a king's bones
Lying like broken sticks among the stones.

ANDREW YOUNG

Winter: East Anglia

In a frosty sunset
  So fiery red with cold
The footballers' onset
  Rings out glad and bold;
Then boys from daily tether
  With famous dogs at heel
In starlight meet together
  And to farther hedges steal;
Where the rats are pattering
  In and out the stacks,
Owls with hatred chattering
  Swoop at the terriers' backs.
And, frost forgot, the chase grows hot
  Till a rat's a foolish prize,
But the cornered weasel stands his ground,
Shrieks at the dogs and boys set round,
Shrieks as he knows they stand all round,
  And hard as winter dies.

EDMUND BLUNDEN

In Hardwood Groves

The same leaves over and over again!
They fall from giving shade above
To make one texture of faded brown
And fit the earth like a leather glove.

45

Before the leaves can mount again
To fill the trees with another shade,
They must go down past things coming up.
They must go down into the dark decayed.

They *must* be pierced by flowers and put
Beneath the feet of dancing flowers.
However it is in some other world
I know that this is the way in ours.

ROBERT FROST

Last Snow

ALTHOUGH the snow still lingers
Heaped on the ivy's blunt webbed fingers
And painting tree-trunks on one side,
Here in this sunlit ride
The fresh unchristened things appear,
Leaf, spathe and stem,
With crumbs of earth clinging to them
To show the way they came
But no flower yet to tell their name,
And one green spear
Stabbing a dead leaf from below
Kills winter at a blow.

ANDREW YOUNG

A Seventeenth-Century Wedding

(Verses from *A Ballad upon a Wedding*)

I TELL thee, Dick, where I have been,
Where I the rarest things have seen;
    O, things without compare!
Such sights again cannot be found
In any place on English ground,
    Be it at wake or fair.

At Charing Cross, hard by the way,
Where we, thou know'st, do sell our hay,
    There is a house with stairs;
And there did I see coming down
Such folk as are not in our town,
    Forty at least, in pairs.

Amongst the rest, one pestilent fine,
His beard no bigger though than thine,
    Walked on before the rest.
Our landlord looks like nothing to him;
The King (God bless him!) 'twould undo him
    Should he go still so dressed.[1]

But wot you what? the youth was going
To make an end of all his wooing;
    The parson for him stayed;
Yet by his leave, for all his haste,
He did not so much wish all past,
    Perchance, as did the maid.

[1] King Charles I himself could not afford to dress so fine every day.

47

The maid—and thereby hangs a tale,
For such a maid no Whitsun ale
    Could ever yet produce—
No grape that's kindly ripe could be
So sound, so plump, so soft as she,
    Nor half so full of juice;

Her finger was so small, the ring
Would not stay on which they did bring,
    It was too wide a peck;
And to say truth—for out it must—
It looked like a great collar, just,
    About our young colt's neck.

Her feet beneath her petticoat,
Like little mice stole in and out,
    As if they feared the light.
But O! she dances such a way
No sun upon an Easter day
    Is half so fine a sight.

He would have kissed her once or twice,
But she would not, she was so nice,
    She would not do it in sight;
And then she looked as who should say
'I will do what I list to-day,
    And you shall do it at night.'

Her cheeks so rare a white was on,
No daisy makes comparison;
  Who sees them is undone.
For streaks of red were mingled there
Such as are on a Katherine pear
  The side that's next the sun.

Her lips were red, and one was thin
Compared to that was next her chin;
  Some bee had stung it newly.
But, Dick, her eyes so guard her face,
I durst no more upon them gaze
  Than on the sun in July.

Her mouth so small when she does speak,
Thou'dst swear her teeth her words did break,
  That they might passage get;
But she so handled still the matter,
They came as good as ours, or better,
  And are not spent a whit.

Just in the nick the cook knocked thrice,
And all the waiters in a trice
  His summons did obey;
Each serving-man with dish in hand
Marched boldly up like our trained band,
  Presented, and away.

When all the meat was on the table,
What man of knife or teeth was able
    To stay to be entreated?
And this the very reason was:
Before the parson could say grace
    The company was seated.

The business of the kitchen's great,
For it is fit that men should eat;
    Nor was it there denied.
Passion o' me! how I run on—
There's that that would be thought upon,
    I trow, besides the bride.

Now hats fly off and youths carouse;
Healths first go round, and then the house,
    The bride's came thick and thick,
And when 'twas named another's health,
Perhaps he made it hers by stealth—
    And who could help it, Dick?

O' the sudden up they rise and dance,
Then sit again and sigh and glance,
    Then dance again and kiss.
Thus several ways the time did pass,
Till every woman wished her place
    And every man wished his.

SIR JOHN SUCKLING

III

David's Lament

(from *The Second Book of Samuel*)

AND David lamented with this lamentation over Saul and
over Jonathan his son:

The beauty of Israel is slain upon thy high places:
   How are the mighty fallen!
Tell it not in Gath
Publish it not in the streets of Askelon;
Lest the daughters of the Philistines rejoice,
Lest the daughters of the uncircumcised triumph.

Ye mountains of Gilboa,
Let there be no dew, neither let there be rain upon you, nor
    fields of offerings:
For there the shield of the mighty is vilely cast away,
The shield of Saul, as though he had not been anointed with oil.
From the blood of the slain, from the fat of the mighty,
The bow of Jonathan turned not back,
And the sword of Saul returned not empty.
Saul and Jonathan were lovely and pleasant in their lives,
And in their death they were not divided:
They were swifter than eagles,
They were stronger than lions.
Ye daughters of Israel, weep over Saul,
Who clothed you in scarlet, with other delights,
Who put on ornaments of gold upon your apparel.
   How are the mighty fallen in the midst of the battle!
O Jonathan, thou wast slain in thine high places.
I am distressed for thee, my brother Jonathan:
Very pleasant hast thou been unto me:
Thy love to me was wonderful,
Passing the love of women.
   How are the mighty fallen,
   And the weapons of war perished!

Lament of Hsi-Chun

About the year 110 B.C. a Chinese Princess named Hsi-Chun was sent, for political reasons, to be the wife of a central Asian nomad King, K'un Mo, king of the Wu-sun. When she got there, she found her husband old and decrepit. He only saw her once or twice a year when they drank a cup of wine together. They could not converse, as they had no language in common.

My people have married me—
In a far corner of Earth:
Sent me away to a strange land,
To the king of the Wu-sun.
A tent is my house,
Of felt are my walls;
Raw flesh my food
With mare's milk to drink.
Always thinking of my own country,
My heart sad within.
Would I were a yellow stork
And could fly to my old home!

ARTHUR WALEY

In Time of Pestilence

ADIEU! farewell earth's bliss!
This world uncertain is:
Fond are life's lustful joys,
Death proves them all but toys.
None from his darts can fly:
I am sick, I must die—
   Lord, have mercy on us!

Rich men, trust not in wealth,
Gold cannot buy you health;
Physic himself must fade;
All things to end are made;
The plague full swift goes by
I am sick, I must die—
   Lord, have mercy on us!

Beauty is but a flower
Which wrinkles will devour:
Brightness falls from the air;
Queens have died young and fair,
Dust hath closed Helen's eye:
I am sick, I must die—
　　Lord, have mercy upon us!

Strength stoops unto the grave,
Worms feed on Hector brave;
Swords may not fight with fate;
Earth still holds ope her gate;
Come! Come! the bells do cry:
I am sick, I must die—
　　Lord, have mercy on us!

Wit with his wantonness,
Tasteth death's bitterness;
Hell's executioner
Hath no ears for to hear
What vain art can reply.
I am sick, I must die—
　　Lord, have mercy on us!

Haste, therefore, each degree
To welcome destiny!
Heaven is our heritage;
Earth but a player's stage.
Mount we unto the sky!
I am sick, I must die—
　　Lord, have mercy on us!

THOMAS NASHE

The Death of Kings

(from *King Richard II*)

FOR God's sake, let us sit upon the ground,
And tell sad stories of the death of kings:—
How some have been deposed; some slain in war;
Some haunted by the ghosts they have deposed;
Some poison'd by their wives; some sleeping kill'd;
All murder'd:—for within the hollow crown
That rounds the mortal temples of a king
Keeps Death his court; and there the antick[1] sits,
Scoffing his state, and grinning at his pomp;
Allowing him a breath, a little scene,
To monarchize, be fear'd, and kill with looks;
Infusing him with self and vain conceit,—
As if this flesh, which walls about our life,
Were brass impregnable; and humour'd thus,
Comes at the last, and with a little pin
Bores through his castle-wall, and—farewell king!

WILLIAM SHAKESPEARE

[1] Buffoon.

At the Round Earth's Imagined Corners

AT the round earth's imagined corners, blow
Your trumpets, angels, and arise, arise
From death, you numberless infinities
Of souls, and to your scattered bodies go;
All whom the flood did, and fire shall o'erthrow,
All whom war, dearth, age, agues, tyrannies,
Despair, law, chance hath slain, and you, whose eyes
Shall behold God, and never taste death's woe.
But let them sleep, Lord, and me mourn a space;
For, if above all these my sins abound,
'Tis late to ask abundance of Thy grace,
When we are there. Here on this lowly ground,
Teach me how to repent, for that's as good
As if thou hadst seal'd my pardon with thy blood.

JOHN DONNE

The Twa Corbies

As I was walking all alane
I heard twa corbies making a mane:[1]
The tane unto the tother say,
'Whar sall we gang and dine to-day?'

'In behint yon auld fail-dyke,
I wot there lies a new-slain knight;
And naebody kens that he lies there
But his hawk, his hound, and his lady fair.

'His hound is to the hunting gane,
His hawk to fetch the wild-fowl hame,
His lady's ta'en anither mate,
So we may mak our dinner sweet.

'Ye'll sit on his white hause-bane,[2]
And I'll pike out his bonnie blue e'en;
Wi' ae lock o' his gowden hair
We'll theek[3] our nest when it grows bare.

'Mony a one for him maks mane,
But nane sall ken whar he is gane;
O'er his white banes, when they are bare,
The wind sall blaw for evermair.'

[1] Moan.   [2] Neck-bone.   [3] Thatch.

Helen of Kirconnell

I WISH I were where Helen lies,
Night and day on me she cries:
O that I were where Helen lies,
  On fair Kirconnell lea!

Curst be the heart that thought the thought,
And curst the hand that fired the shot,
When in my arms burd[1] Helen dropt,
  And died to succour me!

O think na ye my heart was sair,
When my Love dropt and spak nae mair?
There did she swoon wi' meikle[2] care,
  On fair Kirconnell lea.

As I went down the waterside
None but my foe to be my guide,
None but my foe to be my guide,
  On fair Kirconnell lea;

I lighted down, my sword to draw,
I hackèd him in pieces sma',
I hackèd him in pieces sma',
  For her sake that died for me.

[1] Maid.   [2] Much.

O Helen fair, beyond compare!
I'll mak a garland o' thy hair,
Shall bind my heart for evermair,
    Until the day I die.

O that I were where Helen lies!
Night and day on me she cries;
Out of my bed she bids me rise,
    Says, 'Haste, and come to me!'

I wish my grave were growing green,
A winding-sheet drawn owre my een,
And I in Helen's arms lying
    On fair Kirconnell lea.

Great Things

SWEET cyder is a great thing,
    A great thing to me,
Spinning down to Weymouth town
    By Ridgway thirstily,
And maid and mistress summoning
    Who tend the hostelry:
O cyder is a great thing,
    A great thing to me!

The dance it is a great thing,
  A great thing to me,
With candles lit and partners fit
  For night-long revelry;
And going home when day-dawning
  Peeps pale upon the lea:
O dancing is a great thing,
  A great thing to me!

Love is, yea, a great thing,
  A great thing to me,
When, having drawn across the lawn
  In darkness silently,
A figure flits like one a-wing
  Out from the nearest tree:
O love is, yes, a great thing,
  A great thing to me!

Will these be always great things,
     Great things to me? . . .
Let it befall that One will call,
     'Soul, I have need of thee':
What then? Joy-jaunts, impassioned flings,
     Love, and its ecstasy,
Will always have been great things,
     Great things to me!

THOMAS HARDY

The Bust

WHEN I was wandering far from home,
I left a woman in my room
To clean my hearth and floor, and dust
My shelves and pictures, books and bust.

When I came back a welcome glow
Burned in her eyes—her voice was low;
And everything was in its place,
As clean and bright as her own face.

But when I looked more closely there,
The dust was on my dark, bronze hair;
The nose and eyebrows too were white—
And yet the lips were clean and bright.

WILLIAM HENRY DAVIES (1871–1940) BY JACOB EPSTEIN

The years have gone, and so has she,
But still the truth remains with me—
How that hard mouth was once kept clean
By living lips that kissed unseen.

W. H. DAVIES

She Dwelt among the Untrodden Ways

SHE dwelt among the untrodden ways
   Beside the springs of Dove,
A maid whom there were none to praise
   And very few to love:

A violet by a mossy stone
   Half-hidden from the eye!
—Fair as a star, when only one
   Is shining in the sky.

She lived unknown, and few could know
   When Lucy ceased to be;
But she is in her grave, and, oh,
   The difference to me!

WILLIAM WORDSWORTH

Let me not to the Marriage of True Minds

Let me not to the marriage of true minds
Admit impediments. Love is not love
Which alters when it alteration finds,
Or bends with the remover to remove:
O no, it is an ever fixèd mark
That looks on tempests and is never shaken;
It is the star to every wand'ring bark,
Whose worth's unknown, although his height be taken.
Love's not Time's fool, though rosy lips and cheeks
Within his bending sickle's compass come;
Love alters not with his brief hours and weeks,
But bears it out even to the edge of doom.
 If this be error and upon me proved,
 I never writ, nor no man ever loved.

WILLIAM SHAKESPEARE

Stopping by Woods on a Snowy Evening

WHOSE woods these are I think I know.
His house is in the village though;
He will not see me stopping here
To watch his woods fill up with snow.

My little horse must think it queer
To stop without a farmhouse near
Between the woods and frozen lake
The darkest evening of the year.

He gives his harness bells a shake
To ask if there is some mistake.
The only other sound's the sweep
Of easy wind and downy flake.

The woods are lovely, dark and deep,
But I have promises to keep,
And miles to go before I sleep,
And miles to go before I sleep.

ROBERT FROST

On his Blindness

WHEN I consider how my light is spent
  Ere half my days, in this dark world and wide,
  And that one talent which is death to hide
Lodged with me useless, though my soul more bent
To serve therewith my Maker, and present
My true account, lest he returning chide;
'Doth God exact day-labour, light denied?'
I fondly ask. But Patience, to prevent
That murmur, soon replies, 'God doth not need
  Either man's work or his own gifts. Who best
    Bear his mild yoke, they serve him best. His state
Is kingly: thousands at his bidding speed,
  And post o'er land and ocean without rest:
    They also serve who only stand and wait.'

JOHN MILTON

The Old Ships

I HAVE seen old ships sail like swans asleep
  Beyond the village which men still call Tyre,
  With leaden age o'ercargoed, dipping deep
For Famagusta and the hidden sun
That rings black Cyprus with a lake of fire;

67

And all those ships were certainly so old
Who knows how oft with squat and noisy gun,
Questing brown slaves or Syrian oranges,
The pirate Genoese
Hell-raked them till they rolled
Blood, water, fruit and corpses up the hold.
But now through friendly seas they softly run,
Painted the mid-sea blue or shore-sea green,
Still patterned with the vine and grapes in gold.

But I have seen,
Pointing her shapely shadows from the dawn
An image tumbled on a rose-swept bay,
A drowsy ship of some yet older day;
And, wonder's breath indrawn,
Thought I—who knows—who knows—but in that same
(Fished up beyond Aeaea, patched up new
—Stern painted brighter blue—)
That talkative, bald-headed seaman[1] came
(Twelve patient comrades sweating at the oar)
From Troy's doom-crimson shore,
And with great lies about his wooden horse
Set the crew laughing, and forgot his course.
It was so old a ship—who knows, who knows?
—And yet so beautiful, I watched in vain
To see the mast burst open with a rose,
And the whole deck put on its leaves again.

JAMES ELROY FLECKER

[1] Odysseus.

Alarm at first entering the Yang-Tze Gorges

ABOVE, a mountain ten thousand feet high:
Below, a river a thousand fathoms deep.
A strip of sky, walled by cliffs of stone:
Wide enough for the passage of a single reed.
At Chü-t'ang a straight cleft yawns:
At Yen-yü islands block the stream.
Long before night the walls are black with dusk;
Without wind white waves rise.
The big rocks are like a flat sword:
The little rocks resemble ivory tusks.

We are stuck fast and cannot move a step.
How much the less, three hundred miles?
Frail and slender, the twisted-bamboo rope:
Weak, the dangerous hold of the towers' feet.
A single slip—the whole convoy lost:
And *my* life hangs on *this* thread!
I have heard a saying 'He that has an upright heart
Shall walk scathless through the lands of Man and Mo.'
How can I believe that since the world began
In every shipwreck none have drowned by rogues?
And how can I, born in evil days
And fresh from failure, ask a kindness of Fate?
Often I fear that these un-talented limbs
Will be laid at last in an un-named grave!

ARTHUR WALEY
(from the Chinese poem by Po Chü-i)

Paying Calls

I WENT by footpath and by stile
    Beyond where bustle ends,
Strayed here a mile and there a mile
    And called upon some friends.

On certain ones I had not seen
    For years past did I call,
And then on others who had been
    The oldest friends of all.

It was the time of midsummer
    When they had used to roam;
But now, though tempting was the air,
    I found them all at home.

I spoke to one and other of them
    By mound and stone and tree
Of things we had done ere days were dim,
    But they spoke not to me.

THOMAS HARDY

Friends Beyond

WILLIAM Dewy, Tranter[1] Reuben, Farmer Ledlow late at
    plough,
    Robert's kin, and John's, and Ned's,
And the Squire, and Lady Susan, lie in Mellstock churchyard
    now!

'Gone,' I call them, gone for good, that group of local hearts and
    heads;
    Yet at mothy curfew-tide,
And at midnight when the noon-heat breathes it back from walls
    and leads,

They've a way of whispering to me—fellow-wight who yet
    abide—
    In the muted, measured note
Of a ripple under archways, or a lone cave's stillicide:[2]

      [1] Carter.   [2] Dropping of water.

'We have triumphed: this achievement turns the bane to antidote,
  Unsuccesses to success,
Many thought-worn eyes and morrows to a morrow free of
  thought.

'No more need we corn and clothing, feel of old terrestrial stress;
  Chill detraction stirs no sigh;
Fear of death has even bygone us: death gave all that we possess.'

W.D.—'Ye mid burn the old bass-viol that I set such value by.'
  Squire.—'You may hold the manse in fee,
You may wed my spouse, may let my children's memory of me
  die.'

Lady S.—'You may have my rich brocades, my laces; take each
  household key;
  Ransack coffer, desk, bureau;
Quiz the few poor treasures hid there, con the letters kept by me.'

Far.—'Ye mid zell my favourite heifer, ye mid let the charlock
  grow,
  Foul the grinterns,[1] give up thrift.'
Far. Wife.—'If ye break my best blue china, children, I shan't care
  or ho.'

All.—'We've no wish to hear the tidings, how the people's for-
  tunes shift;
  What your daily doings are;
Who are wedded, born, divided; if your lives beat slow or swift.

'Curious not the least are we if our intents you make or mar,
  If you quire to our old tune,
If the City stage still passes, if the weirs still roar afar.'

[1] Granaries.

72

—Thus, with very gods' composure, freed those crosses late and
  soon
  Which, in life, the Trine[1] allow
(Why, none witteth), and ignoring all that haps beneath the
  moon,

William Dewy, Tranter Reuben, Farmer Ledlow late at plough,
  Robert's kin, and John's, and Ned's,
And the Squire, and Lady Susan, murmur mildly to me now.

THOMAS HARDY

[1] Trinity

Fitzwilliam Museum, Cambridge

PORTRAIT OF THOMAS HARDY BY AUGUSTUS JOHN

The Carpenter's Son

'Here the hangman stops his cart:
Now the best of friends must part.
Fare you well, for ill fare I:
Live, lads, and I will die.

'Oh, at home had I but stayed
'Prenticed to my father's trade,
Had I but stuck to plane and adze,
I had not been lost, my lads.

'Then I might have built perhaps
Gallows-trees for other chaps,
Never dangled on my own,
Had I but left ill alone.

'Now, you see, they hang me high
And the people passing by
Stop to shake their fists and curse;
So 'tis come from ill to worse.

'Here hang I, and right and left
Two poor fellows hang for theft:
All the same's the luck we prove,
Though the midmost hangs for love.

'Comrades all, that stand and gaze,
Walk henceforth in other ways;
See my neck and save your own:
Comrades all, leave ill alone.

'Make some day a decent end,
Shrewder fellows than your friend.
Fare you well, for ill fare I:
Live, lads, and I will die.'

A. E. HOUSMAN

The Sailor to his Parrot

THOU foul-mouthed wretch! Why dost thou choose
    To learn bad language, and no good;
Canst thou not say 'The Lord be praised'
    As easy as 'Hell's fire and blood'?

Why didst thou call the gentle priest
    A thief and a damned rogue; and tell
The deacon's wife, who came to pray,
    To hold her jaw and go to hell?

Thou art a foe, no friend of mine,
    For all my thoughts thou givest away;
What'er I say in confidence,
    Thou dost in evil hours betray.

Thy mind's for ever set on bad;
    I cannot mutter one small curse,
But thou dost make it endless song,
    And shout it to a neighbour's house.

Aye, swear to thy delight and ours,
    When here I welcome shipmates home,
And thou canst see abundant grog—
    But hold thy tongue when landsmen come.

75

Be dumb when widow Johnson's near,
    Be dumb until our wedding day;
And after that—but not before—
    She will enjoy the worst you say.

There is a time to speak and not;
    When we're together, all is well;
But damn thy soul—What! you damn *mine*!
    And you tell *me* to go to hell!

                     W. H. DAVIES

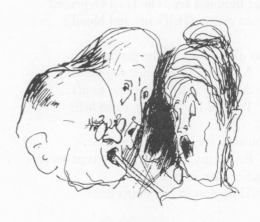

Talk

I WISH people, when you sit near them,
wouldn't think it necessary to make conversation
and send thin draughts of words
blowing down your neck and your ears
and giving you a cold in your inside.

                     D. H. LAWRENCE

Up at a Villa—Down in the City

(as distinguished by an Italian person of quality)

I

HAD I but plenty of money, money enough and to spare,
The house for me, no doubt, were a house in the city-square;
Ah, such a life, such a life, as one leads at the window there!

2

Something to see, by Bacchus, something to hear, at least!
There, the whole day long, one's life is a perfect feast;
While up at a villa one lives, I maintain it, no more than a beast.

3

Well now, look at our villa! stuck like the horn of a bull
Just on a mountain-edge as bare as the creature's skull,
Save a mere shag of a bush with hardly a leaf to pull!
—I scratch my own, sometimes, to see if the hair's turned wool.

4

But the city, of the city—the square with the houses! Why?
They are stone-faced, white as a curd, there's something to take
    the eye!
Houses in four straight lines, not a single front awry;
You watch who crosses and gossips, who saunters, who hurries
    by;
Green blinds, as a matter of course, to draw when the sun gets
    high;
And the shops with fanciful signs which are painted properly.

5

What of a villa? Though winter be over in March by rights,
'Tis May perhaps ere the snow shall have withered well off the
    heights:
You've the brown ploughed land before, where the oxen steam
    and wheeze,
And the hills over-smoked behind by the faint grey olive-trees.

6

Is it better in May, I ask you? You've summer all at once;
In a day he leaps complete with a few strong April suns.
'Mid the sharp short emerald wheat, scarce risen three fingers
    well,
The wild tulip, at end of its tube, blows out its great red bell
Like a thin clear bubble of blood, for the children to pick and sell.

7

Is it ever hot in the square? There's a fountain to spout and splash!
In the shade it sings and springs; in the shine such foam-bows
    flash
On the horses with curling fish-tails, that prance and paddle and
    pash
Round the lady atop in her conch—fifty gazers do not abash,
Though all that she wears is some weeds round her waist in a
    sort of sash.

8

All the year long at the villa, nothing to see though you linger,
Except yon cypress that points like death's lean lifted forefinger.
Some think fireflies pretty, when they mix i' the corn and mingle,
Or thrid the stinking hemp till the stalks of it seem a-tingle.

Late August or early September, the stunning cicala is shrill,
And the bees keep their tiresome whine round the resinous firs on
the hill.
Enough of the seasons,—I spare you the months of the fever and
chill.

9

Ere you open your eyes in the city, the blessed church-bells
begin:
No sooner the bells leave off than the diligence rattles in:
You get the pick of the news, and it costs you never a pin.
By-and-by there's the travelling doctor gives pills, lets blood,
draws teeth;
Or the Pulcinello-trumpet breaks up the market beneath.
At the post-office such a scene-picture—the new play, piping hot!
And a notice how, only this morning, three liberal thieves were
shot.
Above it, behold the Archbishop's most fatherly of rebukes,
And beneath, with his crown and his lion, some little new law of
the Duke's!
Or a sonnet with flowery marge, to the Reverend Don So-and-so
Who is Dante, Boccaccio, Petrarca, Saint Jerome and Cicero,
'And moreover,' (the sonnet goes rhyming,) 'the skirts of Saint
Paul has reached,
'Having preached us those six Lent-lectures more unctuous than
ever he preached.'
Noon strikes,—here sweeps the procession! our Lady borne
smiling and smart
With a pink gauze gown all spangles, and seven swords stuck in
her heart!
Bang-whang-whang goes the drum, tootle-te-tootle the fife;
No keeping one's haunches still: it's the greatest pleasure in life.

But bless you, it's dear—it's dear! fowls, wine, at double the rate.
They have clapped a new tax upon salt, and what oil pays passing
    the gate
It's a horror to think of. And so, the villa for me, not the city!
Beggars can scarcely be choosers: but still—ah, the pity, the pity!
Look, two and two go the priests, then the monks with cowls and
    sandals,
And the penitents dressed in white shirts, a-holding the yellow
    candles;
One, he carries a flag up straight, and another a cross with handles,
And the Duke's guard brings up the rear, for the better prevention
    of scandals:
Bang-whang-whang goes the drum, tootle-te-tootle the fife.
Oh, a day in the city-square, there is no such pleasure in life!

ROBERT BROWNING

The Coming of Good Luck

So good luck came, and on my roof did light
Like noiseless snow, or as the dew of night:
Not all at once, but gently, as the trees
Are by the sunbeams tickled by degrees.

ROBERT HERRICK

The Street Sounds to the Soldiers' Tread

THE street sounds to the soldiers' tread,
  And out we troop to see:
A single redcoat turns his head,
  He turns and looks at me.

My man, from sky to sky's so far,
  We never crossed before;
Such leagues apart the world's ends are,
  We're like to meet no more;

What thoughts at heart have you and I
  We cannot stop to tell;
But dead or living, drunk or dry,
  Soldier, I wish you well.

A. E. HOUSMAN

Nutting

IT seems a day
(I speak of one from many singled out)
One of those heavenly days that cannot die;
When, in the eagerness of boyish hope,
I left our cottage-threshold, sallying forth
With a huge wallet o'er my shoulders slung,
A nutting-crook in hand; and turned my steps
Tow'rd some far-distant wood, a figure quaint,
Tricked out in proud disguise of cast-off weeds
Which for that service had been husbanded.
By exhortation of my frugal dame—
Motley accoutrement, of power to smile
At thorns, and brakes, and brambles,—and in truth
More ragged than need was! O'er pathless rocks,
Through beds of matted fern, and tangled thickets,
Forcing my way, I came to one dear nook
Unvisited, where not a broken bough
Drooped with its withered leaves, ungracious sign
Of devastation; but the hazels rose
Tall and erect, with tempting clusters hung,
A virgin scene!—A little while I stood,
Breathing with such suppression of the heart
As joy delights in; and with wise restraint
Voluptuous, fearless of a rival, eyed
The banquet;—or beneath the trees I sate
Among the flowers, and with the flowers I played;
A temper known to those who, after long

And weary expectation, have been blest
With sudden happiness beyond all hope.
Perhaps it was a bower beneath whose leaves
The violets of five seasons re-appear
And fade, unseen by any human eye;
Where fairy water-breaks do murmur on
For ever; and I saw the sparkling foam,
And—with my cheek on one of those green stones
That, fleeced with moss, under the shady trees,
Lay round me, scattered like a flock of sheep—
I heard the murmur and the murmuring sound,
In that sweet mood when pleasure loves to pay
Tribute to ease; and, of its joy secure,
The heart luxuriates with indifferent things,
Wasting its kindliness on stocks and stones,
And on the vacant air. Then up I rose,
And dragged to earth both branch and bough, with crash
And merciless ravage: and the shady nook
Of hazels, and the green and mossy bower,
Deformed and sullied, patiently gave up
Their quiet being: and unless I now
Confound my present feelings with the past,
Ere from the mutilated bower I turned
Exulting, rich beyond the wealth of kings,
I felt a sense of pain when I beheld
The silent trees, and saw the intruding sky.—
Then, dearest Maiden, move along these shades
In gentleness of heart; with gentle hand
Touch—for there is a spirit in the woods.

WILLIAM WORDSWORTH

To Dianeme

SWEET, be not proud of those two eyes
Which starlike sparkle in their skies;
Nor be you proud, that you can see
All hearts your captives; yours yet free:
Be you not proud of that rich hair
Which wantons with the lovesick air;
When as that ruby which you wear,
Sunk from the tip of your soft ear,
Will last to be a precious stone
When all your world of beauty's gone.

ROBERT HERRICK

84

Ode to the West Wind

O WILD West Wind, thou breath of Autumn's being,
Thou, from whose unseen presence the leaves dead
Are driven, like ghosts from an enchanter fleeing,

Yellow, and black, and pale, and hectic red,
Pestilence-stricken multitudes: O thou,
Who chariotest to their dark wintry bed

The wingèd seeds, where they lie cold and low,
Each like a corpse within its grave, until
Thine azure sister of the Spring shall blow

Her clarion o'er the dreaming earth, and fill
(Driving sweet buds like flocks to feed in air)
With living hues and odours plain and hill:

Wild Spirit, which art moving everywhere;
Destroyer and preserver; hear, O hear!

II

Thou on whose stream, mid the steep sky's commotion,
Loose clouds like earth's decaying leaves are shed,
Shook from the tangled boughs of Heaven and Ocean,

Angels of rain and lightning: there are spread
On the blue surface of thine aëry surge,
Like the bright hair uplifted from the head

Of some fierce Mænad, even from the dim verge
Of the horizon to the zenith's height,
The locks of the approaching storm. Thou dirge

Of the dying year, to which this closing night
Will be the dome of a vast sepulchre,
Vaulted with all thy congregated might

Of vapours, from whose solid atmosphere
Black rain, and fire, and hail will burst: O hear!

III

Thou who didst waken from his summer dreams
The blue Mediterranean, where he lay,
Lull'd by the coil of his crystàlline streams,

Beside a pumice isle in Baiæ's bay,
And saw in sleep old palaces and towers
Quivering within the wave's intenser day,

All overgrown with azure moss and flowers
So sweet, the sense faints picturing them! Thou
For whose path the Atlantic's level powers

Cleave themselves into chasms, while far below
The sea-blooms and the oozy woods which wear
The sapless foliage of the ocean, know

Thy voice, and suddenly grow gray with fear,
And tremble and despoil themselves: O hear!

IV

If I were a dead leaf thou mightest bear;
If I were a swift cloud to fly with thee;
A wave to pant beneath thy power, and share

The impulse of thy strength, only less free
Than thou, O uncontrollable! If even
I were as in my boyhood, and could be

The comrade of thy wanderings over Heaven,
As then, when to outstrip thy skiey speed
Scarce seemed a vision; I would ne'er have striver

As thus with thee in prayer in my sore need.
O lift me as a wave, a leaf, a cloud!
I fall upon the thorns of life! I bleed!

A heavy weight of hours has chain'd and bow'd
One too like thee: tameless, and swift, and proud.

Make me thy lyre, even as the forest is:
What if my leaves are falling like its own!
The tumult of thy mighty harmonies

Will take from both a deep, autumnal tone,
Sweet though in sadness. Be thou, Spirit fierce,
My spirit! Be thou me, impetuous one!

Drive my dead thoughts over the universe
Like wither'd leaves to quicken a new birth!
And, by the incantation of this verse,

Scatter, as from an unextinguish'd hearth
Ashes and sparks, my words among mankind!
Be through my lips to unawaken'd earth

The trumpet of a prophecy! O Wind,
If Winter comes, can Spring be far behind?

PERCY BYSSHE SHELLEY

IV

La Belle Dame sans Merci

'O WHAT can ail thee, knight-at-arms,
 Alone and palely loitering?
The sedge has withered from the lake,
 And no birds sing.

'O what can ail thee, knight-at-arms,
 So haggard and so woe-begone?
The squirrel's granary is full,
 And the harvest's done.

'I see a lily on thy brow
    With anguish moist and fever dew,
And on thy cheeks a fading rose
    Fast withereth too.'

'I met a lady in the meads,
    Full beautiful—a faery's child:
Her hair was long, her foot was light,
    And her eyes were wild.

'I made a garland for her head,
    And bracelets too, and fragrant zone;
She looked at me as she did love,
    And made sweet moan.

'I set her on my pacing steed,
    And nothing else saw all day long,
For sidelong would she bend, and sing
    A faery's song.

'She found me roots of relish sweet,
    And honey wild and manna dew;
And sure in language strange she said,
    "I love thee true."

'She took me to her elfin grot,
    And there she wept, and sighed full sore,
And there I shut her wild, wild eyes
    With kisses four.

'And there she lullèd me asleep,
    And there I dreamed—ah! woe betide!—
The latest dream I ever dreamed
    On the cold hill's side.

'I saw pale kings, and princes too,
    Pale warriors, death pale were they all;
They cried—"La belle Dame sans Merci
    Hath thee in thrall!"

'I saw their starved lips in the gloam
    With horrid warning gapèd wide,
And I awoke, and found me here,
    On the cold hill's side.

'And this is why I sojourn here
    Alone and palely loitering,
Though the sedge is withered from the lake,
    And no birds sing.'

JOHN KEATS

91

Edward

'Why does your brand sae drop wi' blude,
    Edward, Edward?
Why does your brand sae drop wi' blude,
    And why sae sad gang ye, O?'—
'O I hae kill'd my hawk sae gude,
    Mither, mither;
O I hae kill'd my hawk sae gude,
    And I had nae mair but he, O.'

'Your hawk's blude was never sae red,
    Edward, Edward;
Your hawk's blude was never sae red,
    My dear son, I tell thee, O.'—
'O I hae kill'd my red-roan steed,
    Mither, mither;
O I hae kill'd my red-roan steed,
    That erst was sae fair and free, O.'

'Your steed was auld, and ye hae got mair,
    Edward, Edward;
Your steed was auld, and ye hae got mair;
    Some other dule[1] ye dree,[2] O.'—
'O I hae kill'd my father dear,
    Mither, mither;
O I hae kill'd my father dear,
    Alas, and wae is me, O!'

[1] Woe.   [2] Undergo.

'And whatten penance will ye dree for that,
       Edward, Edward?
Whatten penance will ye dree for that?
       My dear son, now tell me, O.'—
'I'll set my feet in yonder boat,
       Mither, mither;
I'll set my feet in yonder boat,
       And I'll fare over the sea, O.'

'And what will ye do wi' your tow'rs and your ha',
       Edward, Edward?
And what will ye do wi' your tow'rs and your ha',
       That were sae fair to see, O?'—
'I'll let them stand till they doun fa',
       Mither, mither;
I'll let them stand till they doun fa',
       For here never mair maun I be, O.'

'And what will ye leave to your bairns and your wife,
       Edward, Edward?
And what will ye leave to your bairns and your wife,
       When ye gang owre the sea, O?'—
'The warld's room: let them beg through life,
       Mither, mither;
The warld's room: let them beg through life;
       For them never mair will I see, O.'

'And what will ye leave to your ain mither dear,
       Edward, Edward?
And what will ye leave to your ain mither dear,
       My dear son, now tell me, O?'—

'The curse of hell frae me sall ye bear,
    Mither, mither;
The curse of hell frae me sall ye bear:
    Sic counsels ye gave to me, O!'

The Daemon Lover

'O WHERE have you been, my long, long love,
    This long seven years and more?'
'O I'm come to seek my former vows
    Ye granted me before.'

'O hold your tongue of your former vows,
　　For they will breed sad strife;
O hold your tongue of your former vows,
　　For I am become a wife.'

He turned him right and round about,
　　And the tear blinded his e'e;
'I would never ha' trodden on Irish ground,
　　If it had na' been for thee.

'I might ha' had a king's daughter,
　　Far, far beyond the sea;
I might have had a king's daughter,
　　Had it not been for love o' thee.'

'If ye might ha' had a king's daughter,
　　Yourself ye had to blame;
Ye might ha' taken the king's daughter
　　For ye kenned that I was nane!

'If I was to leave my husband dear,
　　And my two babes also,
O what have you to take me to,
　　If I with you should go?'

'I ha' seven ships upon the sea;
　　The eighth brought me to land,
With four and twenty bold mariners,
　　And music on every hand.'

She has taken up her two little babes,
 Kissed them both cheek and chin;
'O fare ye well, my own two babes,
 For I'll never see you again.'

She set her foot upon the ship;
 No mariners could she behold,
But the sails were o' the taffety,
 And the masts o' the beaten gold.

She had not sailed a league, a league,
 A league but barely three,
When dismal grew his countenance,
 And drumlie[1] grew his e'e.

They had not sailed a league, a league,
 A league but barely three,
Until she espied his cloven foot,
 And she wept right bitterly.

'O hold your tongue of your weeping,' says he,
 'Of your weeping now let me be;
I will show you how the lilies grow
 On the banks of Italy!'

'O what hills are yon, yon pleasant hills,
 That the sun shines sweetly on?'
'O yon are the hills of heaven,' he said,
 'Where you will never win.'

[1] Gloomy.

O whaten a mountain is yon,' she said,
  'All so dreary wi' frost and snow?'
'O yon is the mountain of hell,' he cried,
  'Where you and I will go.'

He struck the topmast wi' his hand,
  The foremast wi' his knee,
And he brake that gallant ship in twain,
  And sank her in the sea.

Sir John Graham and Barbara Allan

It was in and about the Martinmas time,
  When the green leaves were a-falling,
That Sir John Graham o' the west country
  Fell in love with Barbara Allan.

He sent his men down through the town,
  To the place where she was dwelling.
'O haste and come to my master dear,
  Gin ye be Barbara Allan.'

O slowly, slowly rose she up,
  To the place where he was lying;
And when she drew the curtain by,
  'Young man, I think ye're dying.'

'O it's I'm sick and very, very sick,
  And 'tis a' for Barbara Allan.'
'O the better for me ye's never be,
  Though your heart's blood were a-spilling.

'O dinna ye mind, young man,' said she,
  'When ye war in the tavern a-drinking
How ye made the healths gae round and round,
  And slighted Barbara Allan?'

He turned his face unto the wall,
    And death was with him dealing;
'Adieu! adieu! my dear friends all,
    And be kind to Barbara Allan.'

And slowly, slowly rose she up,
    And slowly, slowly left him;
And sighing said, she could not stay,
    Since death of life had reft him.

She had not gane a mile but twa,
    When she heard the dead-bell ringing,
And every stroke the dead-bell gie'd,
    It cried, Woe to Barbara Allan!

'O mither, mither, mak my bed,
    O mak it saft and narrow:
Since my love died for me to-day,
    I'll die for him to-morrow.'

The Listeners

'Is there anybody there?' said the Traveller,
    Knocking on the moonlit door;
And his horse in the silence champed the grasses
    Of the forest's ferny floor:
And a bird flew up out of the turret,
    Above the Traveller's head:

And he smote upon the door again a second time;
  'Is there anybody there?' he said.
But no one descended to the Traveller;
  No head from the leaf-fringed sill
Leaned over and looked into his grey eyes,
  Where he stood perplexed and still.
But only a host of phantom listeners
  That dwelt in the lone house then
Stood listening in the quiet of the moonlight
  To that voice from the world of men:
Stood thronging the faint moonbeams on the dark stair,
  That goes down to the empty hall,
Hearkening in an air stirred and shaken
  By the lonely Traveller's call.
And he felt in his heart their strangeness,
  Their stillness answering his cry,
While his horse moved, cropping the dark turf,
  'Neath the starred and leafy sky;
For he suddenly smote on the door, even
  Louder, and lifted his head:—
'Tell them I came, and no one answered,
  That I kept my word,' he said.
Never the least stir made the listeners,
  Though every word he spake
Fell echoing through the shadowiness of the still house
  From the one man left awake:
Ay, they heard his foot upon the stirrup,
  And the sound of iron on stone,
And how the silence surged softly backward,
  When the plunging hoofs were gone.

WALTER DE LA MARE

The Ghost in Hamlet

(*Re-enter Ghost*)

Horatio. But, soft, behold! lo, where it comes again!
I'll cross it, though it blast me.—Stay, illusion!
If thou hast any sound, or use of voice,
Speak to me:
If there be any good thing to be done,
That may to thee do ease, and grace to me,
Speak to me:
If thou art privy to thy country's fate,
Which, happily, foreknowing may avoid,
O, speak!
Or if thou hast uphoarded in thy life
Extorted treasure in the womb of earth,
For which, they say, you spirits oft walk in death,
                              (*The cock crows.*)
Speak of it:—stay, and speak!—Stop it, Marcellus.
  Marcellus. Shall I strike at it with my partisan?
  Horatio. Do, if it will not stand.
  Bernardo.   'Tis here!
  Horatio.   'Tis here!
  Marcellus. 'Tis gone!   (*Exit Ghost.*)
We do it wrong, being so majestical,
To offer it the show of violence;

For it is, as the air, invulnerable,
And our vain blows malicious mockery.
    Bernardo. It was about to speak when the cock crew.
    Horatio. And then it started like a guilty thing
Upon a fearful summons. I have heard,
The cock, that is the trumpet to the morn,
Doth with his lofty and shrill-sounding throat
Awake the god of day; and, at his warning,
Whether in sea or fire, in earth or air,
Th' extravagant and erring spirit hies
To his confine: and of the truth herein
This present object made probation.
    Marcellus. It faded on the crowing of the cock.
Some say, that ever 'gainst that season comes
Wherein our Saviour's birth is celebrated,
The bird of dawning singeth all night long:
And then, they say, no spirit dare stir abroad;
The nights are wholesome; then no planets strike,
No fairy takes, nor witch hath power to charm,
So hallow'd and so gracious is the time.
    Horatio. So have I heard, and do in part believe it.
But look, the morn, in russet mantle clad,
Walks o'er the dew of yon high eastern hill:
Break we our watch up: and, by my advice,
Let us impart what we have seen to-night
Unto young Hamlet; for, upon my life,
This spirit, dumb to us, will speak to him:
Do you consent we shall acquaint him with it,
As needful in our loves, fitting our duty?
    Marcellus. Let's do't, I pray; and I this morning know
Where we shall find him most convenient.

WILLIAM SHAKESPEARE
(*Hamlet*, Act I, Scene 1)

Juliet's Defiance

(*Juliet, daughter of Capulet and Lady Capulet, has secretly married Romeo. His sudden banishment overwhelms her with grief, which she pretends is due to the death of a cousin. Her father arranges a marriage for her with a noble suitor, Paris. Her mother comes to tell her the news.*)

Lady Capulet. Why, how now, Juliet!
Juliet.   Madam, I am not well.
Lady Capulet. Evermore weeping for your cousin's death?
We will have vengeance for it, fear thou not:
But now I'll tell thee joyful tidings, girl.
Juliet. And joy comes well in such a needful time:
What are they, I beseech your ladyship?
Lady Capulet. Well, well, thou hast a careful father, child;
One who, to put thee from thy heaviness,
Hath sorted out a sudden day of joy,
That thou expect'st not, nor I lookt not for.

Juliet. Madam, in happy time, what day is that?

Lady Capulet. Marry, my child, early next Thursday morn,
The gallant, young, and noble gentleman,
The County Paris, at Saint Peter's Church,
Shall happily make thee there a joyful bride.

Juliet. Now, by Saint Peter's Church, and Peter too,
He shall not make me there a joyful bride.
I wonder at this haste; that I must wed
Ere he, that should be husband, comes to woo.
I pray you, tell my lord and father, madam,
I will not marry yet. These are news indeed!

Lady Capulet. Here comes your father; tell him so yourself,
And see how he will take it at your hands.

Enter CAPULET *and* Nurse.

Capulet. How now! a conduit, girl? what, still in tears?
Evermore show'ring?
Have you deliver'd to her our decree?

Lady Capulet. Ay, sir; but she will none, she gives you thanks,
I would the fool were married to her grave!

Juliet. Good father, I beseech you on my knees,
Hear me with patience but to speak a word.

Capulet. Hang thee, young baggage! disobedient wretch!
I tell thee what,—get thee to church o' Thursday,
Or never after look me in the face:
Speak not, reply not, do not answer me;
My fingers itch.—Wife, we scarce thought us blest
That God had lent us but this only child;
But now I see this one is one too much,
And that we have a curse in having her:
Out on her, hilding!

Nurse.   God in heaven bless her!—
You are to blame, my lord, to rate her so.

Lady Capulet. You are too hot.

Capulet. God's bread! it makes me mad: day, night, late, early,
At home, abroad, alone, in company,
Waking, or sleeping, still my care hath been
To have her match'd: and having now provided
A gentleman of princely parentage,
Of fair demesnes, youthful, and nobly train'd;
And then to have a wretched puling fool,
To answer—'I'll not wed,—I cannot love,
I am too young,—I pray you, pardon me.'—
But, an you will not wed, I'll pardon you:
Look to't, think on't, I do not use to jest.
Thursday is near; lay hand on heart, advise:
An you be mine, I'll give you to my friend;
An you be not, hang, beg, starve, die in the streets,
For, by my soul, I'll ne'er acknowledge thee.

(*Exit.*

Juliet. Is there no pity sitting in the clouds,
That sees into the bottom of my grief?
O, sweet my mother, cast me not away!
Delay this marriage for a month, a week—
Lady Capulet. Talk not to me, for I'll not speak a word:
Do as thou wilt, for I have done with thee.

(*Exit.*

WILLIAM SHAKESPEARE
(*Romeo and Juliet*, Act III,
Scene 5, abridged.)

The Murder of Duncan

(*Macbeth and Lady Macbeth have decided to win the throne of Scotland by murdering King Duncan while he is a guest in their castle. Lady Macbeth, having previously ensured that the King's bodyguards shall sleep soundly, waits anxiously while Macbeth carries out their plan.*)

Lady Macbeth. That which hath made them drunk hath made
    me bold;
What hath quencht them hath given me fire.—Hark!—Peace!
It was the owl that shriekt, the fatal bellman
Which gives the stern'st good-night.—He is about it:
The doors are open; and the surfeited grooms
Do mock their charge with snores: I have drugg'd their possets,
That death and nature do contend about them,
Whether they live or die.
   Macbeth [*Within*]   Who's there? what, ho!
   Lady Macbeth. Alack, I am afraid they have awaked,
And 'tis not done:—th' attempt, and not the deed
Confounds us.—Hark!—I laid their daggers ready;
He could not miss 'em. Had he not resembled
My father as he slept, I had done't.

Enter MACBETH.

                  My husband!
   Macbeth. I have done the deed.—Didst thou not hear a noise?
   Lady Macbeth. I heard the owl scream and the crickets cry.
Did not you speak?
   Macbeth.   When?
   Lady Macbeth.   Now.

Macbeth.   As I descended?

Lady Macbeth. Ay.

Macbeth. Hark!—

Who lies i' the second chamber?

Lady Macbeth.   Donalbain.

Macbeth. This is a sorry sight.   [*Looking on his hands.*

Lady Macbeth. A foolish thought, to say a sorry sight.

Macbeth. There's one did laugh in's sleep, and one cried
    'Murder!'

That they did wake each other: I stood and heard them:

But they did say their prayers, and addrest them

Again to sleep.

Lady Macbeth. There are two lodged together.

Macbeth. One cried 'God bless us!' and 'Amen!' the other;

As they had seen me, with these hangman's hands:

Listening their fear, I could not say 'Amen!'

When they did say 'God bless us!'

Lady Macbeth.   Consider it not so deeply.

Macbeth. But wherefore could not I pronounce 'Amen'?

I had most need of blessing, and 'Amen'

Stuck in my throat.

Lady Macbeth.   These deeds must not be thought

After these ways; so, it will make us mad.

Macbeth. Methought I heard a voice cry 'Sleep no more!

Macbeth does murder sleep,'—the innocent sleep,

Sleep that knits up the ravell'd sleave of care,

The death of each day's life, sore labour's bath,

Balm of hurt minds, great nature's second course,

Chief nourisher in life's feast,—

Lady Macbeth.   What do you mean?

Macbeth. Still it cried 'Sleep no more!' to all the house:

'Glamis hath murder'd sleep, and therefore Cawdor

Shall sleep no more,—Macbeth shall sleep no more!'

Lady Macbeth. Who was it that thus cried? Why, worthy
    thane,
You do unbend your noble strength, to think
So brainsickly of things.—Go get some water,
And wash this filthy witness from your hand.—
Why did you bring these daggers from the place?
They must lie there: go carry them, and smear
The sleepy grooms with blood.
    Macbeth.   I'll go no more:
I am afraid to think what I have done;
Look on't again I dare not.
    Lady Macbeth.   Infirm of purpose!
Give me the daggers: the sleeping and the dead
Are but as pictures: 'tis the eye of childhood
That fears a painted devil. If he do bleed,
I'll gild the faces of the grooms withal;
For it must seem their guilt.   [*Exit. Knocking within.*
    Macbeth.   Whence is that knocking?
How is't with me, when every noise appals me?
What hands are here? ha! they pluck out mine eyes!
Will all great Neptune's ocean wash this blood
Clean from my hand? No; this my hand will rather
The multitudinous seas incarnadine,
Making the green one red.

WILLIAM SHAKESPEARE
(*Macbeth*, Act II, Scene 2)

Ulysses and His Dog

(from the translation of Homer's *Odyssey*)

THUS, near the gates conferring as they drew,
Argus, the dog, his antient master knew;
He, not unconscious of the voice and tread,
Lifts to the sound his ear, and rears his head.
Bred by Ulysses, nourish'd at his board,
But ah! not fated long to please his Lord!
To him, his swiftness and his strength were vain;
The voice of glory call'd him o'er the main.
'Till then in ev'ry sylvan chace renown'd,
With Argus, Argus, rung the woods around;
With him the youth pursu'd the goat or fawn,
Or trac'd the mazy leveret o'er the lawn.
Now left to man's ingratitude he lay,
Un-housed, neglected in the publick way;
And where on heaps the rich manure was spread,
Obscene with reptiles, took his sordid bed.

He knew his lord; he knew, and strove to meet,
In vain he strove, to crawl, and kiss his feet;
Yet (all he could) his tail, his ears, his eyes
Salute his master, and confess his joys.
Soft pity touch'd the mighty master's soul;
Adown his cheek a tear unbidden stole,
Stole unperceiv'd; he turn'd his head, and dry'd
The drop humane: then thus impassion'd cry'd.

What noble beast in this abandon'd state
Lies here all helpless at Ulysses' gate?

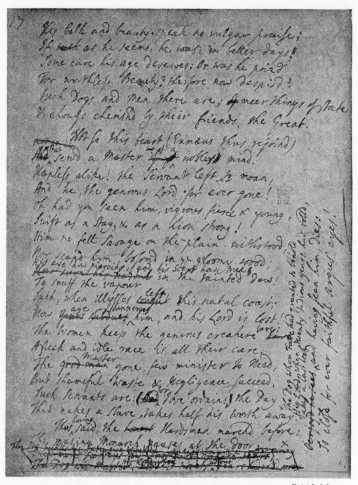

FACSIMILE OF POPE'S MANUSCRIPT

His bulk and beauty speak no vulgar praise;
If, as he seems, he was in better days,
Some care his age deserves: or was he priz'd
For worthless beauty? therefore now despis'd?
Such dogs, and men there are, meer things of state,
And always cherish'd by their friends, the great.

   Not Argus so, (Eumaeus thus rejoin'd)
But served a master of a nobler kind,
Who never, never shall behold him more:
Long, long since perish'd on a distant shore:
Oh had you seen him, vig'rous, bold and young,
Swift as a stag, and as a lion strong,
Him, no fell savage on the plain withstood,
None 'scap'd him, bosom'd in the gloomy wood;
His eye how piercing, and his scent how true,
To winde the vapour in the tainted dew?
Such, when Ulysses left his natal coast;
Now years un-nerve him, and his lord is lost:
The women keep the gen'rous creature bare,
A sleek and idle race is all their care:
The master gone, the servant what restrains?
Or dwells humanity where riot reigns?
Jove fix'd it certain, that whatever day
Makes man a slave, takes half his worth away.

   This said, the honest herdsman strode before:
The musing monarch pauses at the door:
The dog whom fate had granted to behold
His lord, when twenty tedious years had roll'd,
Takes a last look, and having seen him, dies;
So clos'd for ever faithful Argus' eyes.

ALEXANDER POPE

Ulysses

It little profits that an idle king,
By this still hearth, among these barren crags,
Match'd with an aged wife, I mete and dole
Unequal laws unto a savage race,
That hoard, and sleep, and feed, and know not me.
I cannot rest from travel: I will drink
Life to the lees: all times I have enjoy'd
Greatly, have suffer'd greatly, both with those
That loved me, and alone; on shore, and when
Thro' scudding drifts the rainy Hyades
Vext the dim sea: I am become a name;
For always roaming with a hungry heart
Much have I seen and known; cities of men
And manners, climates, councils, governments,
Myself not least, but honour'd of them all;
And drunk delight of battle with my peers,
Far on the ringing plains of windy Troy.
I am a part of all that I have met;
Yet all experience is an arch wherethro'
Gleams that untravell'd world, whose margin fades
For ever and for ever when I move.
How dull it is to pause, to make an end,
To rust unburnish'd, not to shine in use!
As tho' to breathe were life. Life piled on life
Were all too little, and of one to me
Little remains: but every hour is saved
From that eternal silence, something more,

A bringer of new things; and vile it were
For some three suns to store and hoard myself,
And this gray spirit yearning in desire
To follow knowledge, like a sinking star,
Beyond the utmost bound of human thought.

   This is my son, mine own Telemachus,
To whom I leave the sceptre and the isle—
Well-loved of me, discerning to fulfil
This labour, by slow prudence to make mild
A rugged people, and thro' soft degrees
Subdue them to the useful and the good.
Most blameless is he, centred in the sphere
Of common duties, decent not to fail
In offices of tenderness, and pay
Meet adoration to my household gods,
When I am gone. He works his work, I mine.

   There lies the port: the vessel puffs her sail:
There gloom the dark broad seas. My mariners,
Souls that have toil'd, and wrought, and thought with me—
That ever with a frolic welcome took
The thunder and the sunshine, and opposed
Free hearts, free foreheads—you and I are old;
Old age hath yet his honour and his toil;
Death closes all: but something ere the end,
Some work of noble note, may yet be done,
Not unbecoming men that strove with Gods.
The lights begin to twinkle from the rocks:
The long day wanes: the slow moon climbs: the deep
Moans round with many voices. Come, my friends,
'Tis not too late to seek a newer world.
Push off, and sitting well in order smite
The sounding furrows; for my purpose holds
To sail beyond the sunset, and the baths

Of all the western stars, until I die.
It may be that the gulfs will wash us down:
It may be we shall touch the Happy Isles,
And see the great Achilles, whom we knew.
Tho' much is taken, much abides; and tho'
We are not now that strength which in old days
Moved earth and heaven; that which we are, we are;
One equal temper of heroic hearts,
Made weak by time and fate, but strong in will
To strive, to seek, to find, and not to yield.

ALFRED, LORD TENNYSON

Katherine Johnstone

THERE was a may,[1] and a weel-far'd may,
  Lived high up in yon glen;
Her name was Katherine Johnstone
  She was courted by mony men.

Doun cam' the Laird o' Lamington
  Out frae the North Countrie,
All for to court this pretty may,
  Her bridegroom for to be.

He tell'd na her father, he tell'd na her mither,
  He tell'd na ane o' her kin,
But he tell'd the bonnie lass hersel'
  An' her consent did win.

But up then cam' Lord Faughanwood
  Out frae the English Border,

[1] Maid.

And for to court this pretty may,
    A' mounted in good order.

He's tell'd her father, he's tell'd her mither,
    And a' the lave[1] o' her kin;
But he's tell'd na the bonny lass hersel'
    Till on her weddin'-e'en.

She's sent unto her first fere[2] love,
    Gin he would come to see,
And Lamington has sent back word
    Weel answer'd should she be.

Then he has sent a messenger
    Right quietly thro' the land,
For four-and-twenty armèd men
    To ride at his command.

The bridegroom from a high window
    Beheld baith dale and down,
And there he spied her first fere love
    Cam' riding to the toun.

She scoffèd and she scornèd him
    Upon her weddin'-day,
And said it was the Fairy Court
    He saw in sic array!

When a' were at the dinner set,
    Drinking the blude-red wine,
In cam' the Laird o' Lamington
    The bridegroom should hae been.

[1] Rest.   [2] True.

'O come ye here to fight, young lord?
  Or come ye here to play?
Or come ye here to drink good wine
  Upon the weddin'-day?'—

'I come na here to fight,' he said,
  'I come na here to play;
I'll but lead a dance wi' the bonny bride,
  And mount and go my way.'

There was a glass of the blude-red wine
  Was fill'd them up between,
But aye she drank to Lamington,
  Wha her true love had been.

He's ta'en her by the milk-white hand,
  And by the grass-green sleeve;
He's mounted her high behind himsel',
  At her kin he's spier'd¹ nae leave.

There were four-and-twenty bonny boys
  A' clad in the Johnstone grey,
They swore they would tak' the bride again
  By the strong hand, if they may.

It's up, it's up the Cowden bank,
  It's down the Cowden brae;
The bride she gar'd² the trumpet sound
  'It is a weel-won play!'

The blude ran down by Cowden bank
  And down by Cowden brae,

¹ Asked.   ² Made.

116

But aye she gar'd the trumpet sound
  'It's a' fair play!'

'My blessing on your heart, sweet thing!
  Wae to your wilfu' will!
Sae mony a gallant gentleman's blood
  This day as ye've gar'd spill.'

But a' you lords of fair England,
  If you be English born,
Come never to Scotland to seek a wife
  Or else ye'll get the scorn.

They'll haik ye up, and settle ye by,[1]
  Until your weddin'-day;
Then gie ye frogs instead o' fish,
  And do ye foul, foul play.

[1] Lead you on and keep you waiting.

The General

'GOOD-MORNING; good-morning!' the General said
When we met him last week on our way to the line.
Now the soldiers he smiled at are most of 'em dead,
And we're cursing his staff for incompetent swine.
'He's a cheery old card,' grunted Harry to Jack
As they slogged up to Arras[1] with rifle and pack.
    .   .   .

But he did for them both by his plan of attack.

SIEGFRIED SASSOON

[1] The Battle of Arras, fought between Germany and the Allies in the Spring of 1917, involved heavy British casualties.

VISCOUNT NELSON (1758–1805)
from a painting by L. Acquarone after L. Guzzardi

118

1805

AT Viscount Nelson's lavish funeral,
    While the mob milled and yelled about St. Paul's,
A General chatted with an Admiral:

'One of your Colleagues, Sir, remarked to-day
    That Nelson's *exit*, though to be lamented,
Falls not inopportunely, in its way.'

'He was a thorn in our flesh,' came the reply—
    'The most bird-witted, unaccountable,
Odd little runt that ever I did spy.

'One arm, one peeper, vain as Pretty Poll,
    A meddler, too, in foreign politics
And gave his heart in pawn to a plain moll.

'He would dare lecture us Sea Lords, and then
    Would treat his ratings as though men of honour
And play at leap-frog with his midshipmen!

'We tried to box him down, but up he popped,
    And when he'd banged Napoleon at the Nile
Became too much the hero to be dropped.

'You've heard that Copenhagen "blind eye" story?
    We'd tied him to Nurse Parker's apron-strings—
By G-d, he snipped them through and snatched the glory!'

'Yet,' cried the General, 'six-and-twenty sail
    Captured or sunk by him off Trafalgar—
That writes a handsome *finis* to the tale.'

'Handsome enough. The seas are England's now.
    That fellow's foibles need no longer plague us.
He died most creditably, I'll allow.'

'And, Sir, the secret of his victories?'
    'By his unServicelike, familiar ways, Sir,
He made the whole Fleet love him, damn his eyes!'

ROBERT GRAVES

V

Kubla Khan

IN Xanadu did Kubla Khan
  A stately pleasure-dome decree:
Where Alph, the sacred river, ran
Through caverns measureless to man
  Down to a sunless sea.
So twice five miles of fertile ground
With walls and towers were girdled round:
And there were gardens bright with sinuous rills,
Where blossomed many an incense-bearing tree;
And here were forests ancient as the hills,
Enfolding sunny spots of greenery.

But oh! that deep romantic chasm which slanted
Down the green hill athwart a cedarn cover!
A savage place! as holy and enchanted
As e'er beneath a waning moon was haunted
By woman wailing for her demon-lover!
And from this chasm, with ceaseless turmoil seething,
As if this earth in fast thick pants were breathing,
A mighty fountain momently was forced:
Amid whose swift half-intermitted burst
Huge fragments vaulted like rebounding hail,
Or chaffy grain beneath the thresher's flail:
And 'mid these dancing rocks at once and ever
It flung up momently the sacred river.
Five miles meandering with a mazy motion
Through wood and dale the sacred river ran.
Then reached the caverns measureless to man,
And sank in tumult to a lifeless ocean:
And 'mid this tumult Kubla heard from far
Ancestral voices prophesying war!

The shadow of the dome of pleasure
Floated midway on the waves;
    Where was heard the mingled measure
    From the fountain and the caves.
It was a miracle of rare device,
A sunny pleasure-dome with caves of ice!

A damsel with a dulcimer
In a vision once I saw:
It was an Abyssinian maid,
And on her dulcimer she played,

Singing of Mount Abora.
Could I revive within me
Her symphony and song,
To such a deep delight 'twould win me,
That with music loud and long,
I would build that dome in air,
That sunny dome! those caves of ice!
And all who heard should see them there,
And all should cry, Beware! Beware!
His flashing eyes, his floating hair!
Weave a circle round him thrice,
And close your eyes with holy dread,
For he on honey-dew hath fed,
And drunk the milk of Paradise.

SAMUEL TAYLOR COLERIDGE

The Unemployed

No man has hired us
With pocketed hands
And lowered faces
We stand about in open places
And shiver in unlit rooms.
Only the wind moves
Over empty fields, untilled
Where the plough rests, at an angle
To the furrow. In this land
There shall be one cigarette to two men,
To two women one half pint of bitter
Ale. In this land
No man has hired us.
Our life is unwelcome, our death
Unmentioned in 'The Times'.

T. S. ELIOT

Miners

THERE was a whispering in my hearth,
    A sigh of the coal,
Grown wistful of a former earth
    It might recall.

I listened for a tale of leaves
    And smothered ferns;
Frond-forests; and the low, sly lives
    Before the fawns.

My fire might show steam-phantoms simmer
    From Time's old cauldron,
Before the birds made nests in summer,
    Or men had children.

But the coals were murmuring of their mine,
    And moans down there
Of boys that slept wry sleep, and men
    Writhing for air.

And I saw white bones in the cinder-shard.
    Bones without number;
For many hearts with coal are charred
    And few remember.

I thought of some who worked dark pits
    Of war, and died
Digging the rock where Death reputes
    Peace lies indeed.

Comforted years will sit soft-chaired
      In rooms of amber;
The years will stretch their hands, well-cheered
      By our lives' ember.

The centuries will burn rich loads
      With which we groaned,
Whose warmth shall lull their dreaming lids
      While songs are crooned.
But they will not dream of us poor lads
      Lost in the ground.

WILFRED OWEN

Shylock

(from *The Merchant of Venice*)

SIGNOR ANTONIO, many a time and oft,
In the Rialto, you have rated me
About my moneys and my usances:
Still have I borne it with a patient shrug;
For sufferance is the badge of all our tribe:
You call me misbeliever, cut-throat dog,
And spit upon my Jewish gaberdine,
And all for use of that which is mine own.
Well, then, it now appears you need my help:
Go to, then; you come to me, and you say,
'Shylock, we would have moneys':—you say so;
You, that did void your rheum upon my beard,
And foot me as you spurn a stranger cur
Over your threshold: moneys is your suit.
What should I say to you? Should I not say,
'Hath a dog money? is it possible
A cur can lend three thousand ducats?' or
Shall I bend low, and in a bondman's key,
With bated breath and whispering humbleness,
Say this,—
'Fair sir, you spit on me on Wednesday last;
You spurned me such a day; another time
You call'd me dog; and for these courtesies
I'll lend you thus much moneys?'

WILLIAM SHAKESPEARE

Virtue

SWEET day, so cool, so calm, so bright,
The bridal of the earth and sky,
The dew shall weep thy fall to-night;
    For thou must die.

Sweet rose, whose hue angry and brave
Bids the rash gazer wipe his eye,
Thy root is ever in its grave;
    And thou must die.

Sweet spring, full of sweet days and roses,
A box where sweets compacted lie,
My music shows ye have your closes,
    And all must die.

Only a sweet and virtuous soul,
Like seasoned timber, never gives;
But though the whole world turn to coal,
    Then chiefly lives.

GEORGE HERBERT

Animals

(from *Songs of Myself*)

I THINK I could turn and live with animals, they are so placid and
    self-contain'd,
I stand and look at them long and long.

They do not sweat and whine about their condition,
They do not lie awake in the dark and weep for their sins,
They do not make me sick discussing their duty to God,
Not one is dissatisfied, not one is demented with the mania of
    owning things,
Not one kneels to another, nor to his kind that lived thousands of
    years ago,
Not one is respectable or unhappy over the whole earth.

WALT WHITMAN

The World is too much with us

THE world is too much with us; late and soon,
  Getting and spending, we lay waste our powers;
  Little we see in Nature that is ours;
We have given our hearts away, a sordid boon!

This Sea that bares her bosom to the moon,
  The winds that will be howling at all hours
  And are up-gather'd now like sleeping flowers,
For this, for everything, we are out of tune;

It moves us not.—Great God! I'd rather be
  A Pagan suckled in a creed outworn,
So might I, standing on this pleasant lea,

  Have glimpses that would make me less forlorn;
Have sight of Proteus rising from the sea;
  Or hear old Triton blow his wreathèd horn.

WILLIAM WORDSWORTH

The Joy of Life

(David sings to Saul)

OH, the wild joys of living! the leaping from rock up to rock—
The strong rending of boughs from the fir-tree,—the cool silver
    shock
Of the plunge in a pool's living water,—the hunt of the bear,
And the sultriness showing the lion is couched in his lair.
And the meal—the rich dates—yellowed over with gold dust
    divine,
And the locust's-flesh steeped in the pitcher; the full draught of
    wine,
And the sleep in the dried river-channel where bull-rushes tell
That the water was wont to go warbling so softly and well.
How good is man's life, the mere living! how fit to employ
All the heart and the soul and the senses, for ever in joy!

ROBERT BROWNING

The Glories of our Blood and State

THE glories of our blood and state
　Are shadows, not substantial things,
There is no armour against fate,
　Death lays his icy hand on kings;
　　Sceptre and crown
　　Must tumble down,
And in the dust be equal made
With the poor crooked scythe and spade.

Some men with swords may reap the field,
　And plant fresh laurels where they kill,
But their strong nerves at last must yield,
　They tame but one another still;
　　Early or late,
　　They stoop to fate,
And must give up their murmuring breath,
When they, pale captives, creep to death.

The garlands wither on your brow,
　Then boast no more your mighty deeds,
Upon Death's purple altar now,
　See, where the victor-victim bleeds;
　　Your heads must come
　　To the cold tomb;
Only the actions of the just
Smell sweet, and blossom in their dust.

JAMES SHIRLEY

Ozymandias

I MET a traveller from an antique land
Who said: Two vast and trunkless legs of stone
Stand in the desert. . . . Near them, on the sand,
Half sunk, a shattered visage lies, whose frown,
And wrinkled lip, and sneer of cold command,
Tell that its sculptor well those passions read
Which yet survive, stamped on these lifeless things,
The hand that mocked them, and the heart that fed;
And on the pedestal these words appear:
'My name is Ozymandias, king of kings:
Look on my works, ye Mighty, and despair!'
Nothing beside remains. Round the decay
Of that colossal wreck, boundless and bare
The lone and level sands stretch far away.

PERCY BYSSHE SHELLEY

O Bruadair

I WILL sing no more songs! The pride of my country I sang
Through forty long years of good rhyme, without any avail;
And no one cared even the half of the half of a hang
For the song or the singer—so, here is an end to the tale!

If you say, if you think, I complain, and have not got a cause,
Let you come to me here, let you look at the state of my hand!
Let you say if a goose-quill has calloused these horny old paws,
Or the spade that I grip on, and dig with, out there in the land?

When our nobles were safe and renowned and were rooted and
    tough,
Though my thought went to them and had joy in the fortune of
    those,
And pride that was proud of their pride—they gave little enough!
Not as much as two boots for my feet, or an old suit of clothes!

I ask of the Craftsman that fashioned the fly and the bird;
Of the Champion whose passion will lift me from death in a
    time;
Of the Spirit that melts icy hearts with the wind of a word,
That my people be worthy, and get, better singing than mine.

I had hoped to live decent, when Ireland was quit of her care,
As a poet or steward, perhaps, in a house of degree,
But the end of the tale is—old brogues and old breeches to wear!
So I'll sing no more songs for the men that care nothing for me.

JAMES STEPHENS

The Big Rug

THAT so many of the poor should suffer from
    cold what can we do to prevent?
To bring warmth to a single body is not much use.
I wish I had a big rug ten thousand feet long,
Which at one time could cover up every inch of the
    City.

ARTHUR WALEY

Let us be Men

FOR God's sake, let us be men
not monkeys minding machines
or sitting with our tails curled
while the machine amuses us, the radio or
    film or gramophone.

Monkeys with a bland grin on our faces.—

D. H. LAWRENCE

Death of a Neighbour

THERE's been a death in the opposite house
As lately as today.
I know it by the numb look
Such houses have alway.

The neighbours rustle in and out;
The doctor drives away.
A window opens like a pod,
Abrupt, mechanically;

Somebody flings a mattress out.
The children hurry by;
They wonder if it died on that.
I used to, when a boy.

The minister goes stiffly in
As if the house were his
And he owned all the mourners now,
And little boys besides;

And then the milliner, and the man
Of the appalling trade
To take the measure of the house.
There'll be that dark parade

Of tassels and of coaches soon.
It's easy as a sign—
   The intuition of the news
   In Just a country town.

EMILY DICKINSON

Song's Eternity

WHAT is song's eternity?
  Come and see.
Can it noise and bustle be?
  Come and see.
Praises sung or praises said
  Can it be?
Wait awhile and these are dead—
  Sigh, sigh;
Be they high or lowly bred
  They die.

What is song's eternity?
  Come and see,
Melodies of earth and sky,
  Here they be.
Song once sung to Adam's ears
  Can it be?
Ballads of six thousand years
  Thrive, thrive;
Songs awakened with the spheres
  Alive.

Mighty songs that miss decay,
   What are they?
Crowds and cities pass away
   Like a day.
Books are writ and books are read;
   What are they?
Years will lay them with the dead—
   Sigh, sigh;
Trifles unto nothing wed,
   They die.

Dreamers, list the honey-bee;
   Mark the tree
Where the bluecap, 'tootle tee,'
   Sings a glee
Sung to Adam and to Eve—
   Here they be.
When floods covered every bough,
   Noah's ark
Heard that ballad singing now;
   Hark, hark,

'Tootle tootle tootle tee'—
   Can it be
Pride and fame must shadows be?
   Come and see—
Every season owns her own;
   Bird and bee
Sing creation's music on;
   Nature's glee
Is in every mood and tone
   Eternity.

The eternity of song
   Liveth here;
Nature's universal tongue
   Singeth here
Songs I've heard and felt and seen
   Everywhere;
Songs like the grass are evergreen:
   The giver
Said 'Live and be'—and they have been,
   For ever.

JOHN CLARE

Music

(from *The Merchant of Venice*)

Lorenzo. How sweet the moonlight sleeps upon this bank!
Here will we sit, and let the sounds of music
Creep in our ears: soft stillness and the night
Become the touches of sweet harmony.

Sit, Jessica: look, how the floor of heaven
Is thick inlaid with patens of bright gold:
There's not the smallest orb which thou behold'st
But in his motion like an angel sings,
Still quiring to the young-eyed cherubins;
Such harmony is in immortal souls;
But, whilst this muddy vesture of decay
Doth grossly close it in, we cannot hear it.
Come, ho! and wake Diana with a hymn:
With sweetest touches pierce your mistress' ear,
And draw her home with music.   [*Music.*
  Jessica. I am never merry when I hear sweet music.
  Lorenzo. The reason is, your spirits are attentive:
For do but note a wild and wanton herd,
Or race of youthful and unhandled colts,
Fetching mad bounds, bellowing and neighing loud,
Which is the hot condition of their blood;
If they but hear perchance a trumpet sound,
Or any air of music touch their ears,
You shall perceive them make a mutual stand,
Their savage eyes turn'd to a modest gaze
By the sweet power of music: therefore the poet
Did feign that Orpheus drew trees, stones, and floods;
Since nought so stockish, hard, and full of rage,
But music for the time doth change his nature.
The man that hath no music in himself,
Nor is not mov'd with concord of sweet sounds,
Is fit for treasons, stratagems, and spoils;
The motions of his spirit are dull as night,
And his affections dark as Erebus:
Let no such man be trusted. Mark the music.

WILLIAM SHAKESPEARE

LATE EIGHTEENTH-CENTURY ILLUSTRATION TO
GRAY'S ELEGY
drawn by William Hamilton and engraved by
James Heath

Elegy written in a Country Churchyard

THE curfew tolls the knell of parting day,
  The lowing herd wind slowly o'er the lea,
The plowman homeward plods his weary way,
  And leaves the world to darkness and to me.

Now fades the glimmering landscape on the sight,
  And all the air a solemn stillness holds,
Save where the beetle wheels his droning flight,
  And drowsy tinklings lull the distant folds:

Save that from yonder ivy-mantled tower
  The moping owl does to the moon complain
Of such as wand'ring near her secret bower
  Molest her ancient solitary reign.

Beneath those rugged elms, that yew-tree's shade
  Where heaves the turf in many a mould'ring heap,
Each in his narrow cell for ever laid,
  The rude forefathers of the hamlet sleep.

The breezy call of incense-breathing morn,
  The swallow twitt'ring from the straw-built shed,
The cock's shrill clarion, or the echoing horn,
  No more shall rouse them from their lowly bed.

For them no more the blazing hearth shall burn,
  Or busy housewife ply her evening care:
No children run to lisp their sire's return,
  Or climb his knees the envied kiss to share.

Oft did the harvest to their sickle yield,
  Their furrow oft the stubborn glebe has broke;
How jocund did they drive their team afield!
  How bow'd the woods beneath their sturdy stroke!

Let not ambition mock their useful toil,
  Their homely joys, and destiny obscure;
Nor grandeur hear with a disdainful smile
  The short and simple annals of the poor.

The boast of heraldry, the pomp of power,
  And all that beauty, all that wealth e'er gave,
Await alike th' inevitable hour:
  The paths of glory lead but to the grave.

Nor you, ye proud, impute to these the fault,
  If memory o'er their tomb no trophies raise,
Where through the long-drawn aisle and fretted vault
  The pealing anthem swells the note of praise.

Can storied urn or animated bust
  Back to its mansion call the fleeting breath?
Can honour's voice provoke the silent dust,
  Or flattery soothe the dull cold ear of death?

Perhaps in this neglected spot is laid
  Some heart once pregnant with celestial fire;
Hands that the rod of empire might have sway'd,
  Or waked to ecstasy the living lyre:

But knowledge to their eyes her ample page
  Rich with the spoils of time did ne'er unroll;
Chill penury repress'd their noble rage,
  And froze the genial current of the soul.

Full many a gem of purest ray serene
  The dark unfathom'd caves of ocean bear:
Full many a flower is born to blush unseen,
  And waste its sweetness on the desert air.

Some village-Hampden, that with dauntless breast
  The little tyrant of his fields withstood,
Some mute inglorious Milton here may rest,
  Some Cromwell, guiltless of his country's blood.

Th' applause of list'ning senates to command,
  The threats of pain and ruin to despise,
To scatter plenty o'er a smiling land,
  And read their history in a nation's eyes,

Their lot forbad: nor circumscribed alone
  Their growing virtues, but their crimes confined;
Forbad to wade through slaughter to a throne,
  And shut the gates of mercy on mankind;

The struggling pangs of conscious truth to hide,
  To quench the blushes of ingenuous shame,
Or heap the shrine of luxury and pride
  With incense kindled at the muse's flame.

Far from the madding crowd's ignoble strife,
  Their sober wishes never learn'd to stray;
Along the cool sequester'd vale of life
  They kept the noiseless tenour of their way.

Yet ev'n these bones from insult to protect
  Some frail memorial still erected nigh,
With uncouth rhymes and shapeless sculpture deck'd,
  Implores the passing tribute of a sigh.

Their name, their years, spelt by th' unletter'd Muse,
  The place of fame and elegy supply:
And many a holy text around she strews
  That teach the rustic moralist to die.

For who, to dumb forgetfulness a prey,
  This pleasing anxious being e'er resign'd,
Left the warm precincts of the cheerful day,
  Nor cast one longing lingering look behind?

On some fond breast the parting soul relies,
  Some pious drops the closing eye requires;
Ev'n from the tomb the voice of nature cries,
  Ev'n in our ashes live their wonted fires

For thee, who, mindful of th' unhonour'd dead,
   Dost in these lines their artless tale relate;
If chance, by lonely contemplation led,
   Some kindred spirit shall inquire thy fate,—

Haply some hoary-headed swain may say,
   'Oft have we seen him at the peep of dawn
Brushing with hasty steps the dews away
   To meet the sun upon the upland lawn.

'There at the foot of yonder nodding beech
   That wreathes its old fantastic roots so high,
His listless length at noontide would he stretch,
   And pore upon the brook that babbles by.

'Hard by yon wood, now smiling as in scorn,
   Mutt'ring his wayward fancies he would rove,
Now drooping, woeful wan, like one forlorn,
   Or crazed with care, or cross'd in hopeless love.

'One morn I miss'd him on the custom'd hill,
   Along the heath, and near his favourite tree;
Another came; nor yet beside the rill,
   Nor up the lawn, nor at the wood was he;

The next, with dirges due in sad array
   Slow through the church-way path we saw him borne:—
Approach and read (for thou canst read) the lay
   Graved on the stone beneath yon aged thorn.'

The Epitaph

Here rests his head upon the lap of Earth
    A Youth, to Fortune and to Fame unknown;
Fair Science frown'd not on his humble birth,
    And Melancholy mark'd him for her own.

Large was his bounty, and his soul sincere;
    Heaven did a recompense as largely send:
He gave to Misery all he had, a tear,
    He gain'd from Heaven, 'twas all he wish'd, a friend.

No farther seek his merits to disclose,
    Or draw his frailties from their dread abode,
(There they alike in trembling hope repose,)
    The bosom of his Father and his God.

THOMAS GRAY

VII

The Rime of the Ancient Mariner

PART I

IT is an ancient Mariner,
And he stoppeth one of three.
'By thy long grey beard and glittering eye,
Now wherefore stopp'st thou me?

The Bridegroom's doors are open'd wide,
And I am next of kin;
The guests are met, the feast is set:
May'st hear the merry din.'

An ancient
Mariner meeteth
three gallants
bidden to a
wedding-feast
and detaineth
one.

He holds him with his skinny hand,
'There was a ship,' quoth he.
'Hold off! unhand me, grey-beard loon!'
Eftsoons his hand dropt he.

He holds him with his glittering eye—
The Wedding-Guest stood still,
And listens like a three years' child:
The Mariner hath his will.

The Wedding-Guest is spellbound by the eye of the old seafaring man, and constrained to hear his tale.

The Wedding-Guest sat on a stone:
He cannot choose but hear;
And thus spake on that ancient man,
The bright-eyed Mariner:

'The ship was cheer'd, the harbour clear'd,
Merrily did we drop
Below the kirk, below the hill,
Below the lighthouse top.

The Sun came up upon the left,
Out of the sea came he!
And he shone bright, and on the right
Went down into the sea.

The Mariner tells how the ship sailed southward with a good wind and fair weather, till it reached the Line.

Higher and higher every day,
Till over the mast at noon——'
The Wedding-Guest here beat his breast,
For he heard the loud bassoon.

The bride hath paced into the hall,
Red as a rose is she;
Nodding their heads before her goes
The merry minstrelsy.

The Wedding-
Guest heareth
the bridal
music; but the
Mariner con-
tinueth his tale.

The Wedding-Guest he beat his breast,
Yet he cannot choose but hear;
And thus spake on that ancient man,
The bright-eyed Mariner:

'And now the Storm-blast came, and he
Was tyrannous and strong:
He struck with his o'ertaking wings,
And chased us south along.

The ship driven
by a storm to-
ward the South
Pole.

With sloping masts and dipping prow,
As who pursued with yell and blow
Still treads the shadow of his foe,
And forward bends his head,
The ship drove fast, loud roar'd the blast,
And southward aye we fled.

And now there came both mist and snow
And it grew wondrous cold:
And ice, mast-high, came floating by,
As green as emerald.

And through the drifts the snowy clifts
Did send a dismal sheen:
Nor shapes of men nor beasts we ken—
The ice was all between.

The land of ice,
and of fearful
sounds, where
no living thing
was to be seen.

The ice was here, the ice was there,
The ice was all around:
It crack'd and growl'd, and roar'd and howl'd,
Like noises in a swound!

At length did cross an Albatross,
Thorough the fog it came;
As if it had been a Christian soul,
We hail'd it in God's name.

It ate the food it ne'er had eat,
And round and round it flew.
The ice did split with a thunder-fit;
The helmsman steer'd us through!

And a good south wind sprung up behind;
The Albatross did follow,
And every day, for food or play,
Came to the mariners' hollo!

In mist or cloud, on mast or shroud,
It perch'd for vespers nine;
Whiles all the night, through fog-smoke white,
Glimmer'd the white moonshine.'

'God save thee, ancient Mariner,
From the fiends, that plague thee thus!—
Why look'st thou so?'—'With my crossbow
I shot the Albatross.

PART II

'The Sun now rose upon the right:
Out of the sea came he,
Still hid in mist, and on the left
Went down into the sea.

And the good south wind still blew behind,
But no sweet bird did follow,
Nor any day for food or play
Came to the mariners' hollo!

And I had done a hellish thing,
And it would work 'em woe:
For all averr'd I had kill'd the bird
That made the breeze to blow.
Ah wretch! said they, the bird to slay
That made the breeze to blow!

His shipmates cry out against the ancient Mariner for killing the bird of good luck.

Nor dim nor red, like God's own head,
The glorious Sun uprist:
Then all averr'd I had kill'd the bird
That brought the fog and mist.
'Twas right, said they, such birds to slay,
That bring the fog and mist.

But when the fog cleared off, they justify the same, and thus make themselves accomplices in the crime.

The fair breeze blew, the white foam flew,
The furrow follow'd free;
We were the first that ever burst
Into that silent sea.

The fair breeze continues; the ship enters the Pacific Ocean and sails northward, even till it reaches the Line.

Down dropt the breeze, the sails dropt down,
'Twas sad as sad could be;
And we did speak only to break
The silence of the sea!

The ship hath been suddenly becalmed.

All in a hot and copper sky,
The bloody Sun, at noon,
Right up above the mast did stand,
No bigger than the Moon.

Day after day, day after day,
We stuck, nor breath nor motion;
As idle as a painted ship
Upon a painted ocean.

Water, water, everywhere,
And all the boards did shrink;
Water, water, everywhere,
Nor any drop to drink.

And the Albatross begins to be avenged.

The very deep did rot: O Christ!
That ever this should be!
Yea, slimy things did crawl with legs
Upon the slimy sea.

About, about, in reel and rout
The death-fires danced at night;
The water, like a witch's oils,
Burnt green, and blue, and white.

And some in dreams assurèd were
Of the Spirit that plagued us so;
Nine fathom deep he had follow'd us
From the land of mist and snow.

And every tongue, through utter drought,
Was wither'd at the root;
We could not speak, no more than if
We had been choked with soot.

Ah! well-a-day! what evil looks
Had I from old and young!
Instead of the cross, the Albatross
About my neck was hung.

A Spirit had followed them: one of the invisible inhabitants of this planet, neither departed souls nor angels; concerning whom the learned Jew, Josephus, and the Platonic Constantinopolitan Michael Psellus, may be consulted. They are very numerous, and there is no climate or element without one or more.

The shipmates, in their sore distress, would fain throw the whole guilt on the ancient Mariner: in sign whereof they hang the dead sea-bird round his neck

PART III

'There passed a weary time. Each throat
Was parch'd, and glazed each eye.
A weary time! a weary time!
How glazed each weary eye!
When looking westward, I beheld
A something in the sky.

The ancient Mariner beholdeth a sign in the element afar off.

At first it seem'd a little speck,
And then it seem'd a mist;
It moved and moved, and took at last
A certain shape, I wist.

155

A speck, a mist, a shape, I wist!
And still it near'd and near'd:
As if it dodged a water-sprite,
It plung'd, and tack'd, and veer'd.

With throats unslaked, with black lips baked,
We could nor laugh nor wail;
Through utter drought all dumb we stood!
I bit my arm, I suck'd the blood,
And cried, "A sail! a sail!"

At its nearer
approach, it
seemeth him
to be a ship;
and at a dear
ransom he
freeth his
speech from
the bonds of
thirst.

With throats unslaked, with black lips baked,
Agape they heard me call:
Gramercy! they for joy did grin,
And all at once their breath drew in,
As they were drinking all.

A flash of joy!

See! see! (I cried) she tacks no more!
Hither to work us weal—
Without a breeze, without a tide,
She steadies with upright keel!

And horror
follows. For
can it be a
ship that comes
onward without
wind or tide?

The western wave was all aflame,
The day was wellnigh done!
Almost upon the western wave
Rested the broad, bright Sun;
When that strange shape drove suddenly
Betwixt us and the Sun.

And straight the Sun was fleck'd with bars

It seemeth him but the skeleton of a ship.

(Heaven's Mother send us grace!)
As if through a dungeon-grate he peer'd
With broad and burning face.

Alas! (thought I, and my heart beat loud)
How fast she nears and nears!
Are those her sails that glance in the Sun,
Like restless gossameres?

Are those her ribs through which the Sun

And its ribs are seen as bars on the face of the setting Sun. The Spectre-Woman and her Death-mate, and no other, on board the skeleton ship. Like vessel, like crew!

Did peer, as through a grate?
And is that Woman all her crew?
Is that a Death? and are there two?
Is Death that Woman's mate?

Her lips were red, her looks were free,
Her locks were yellow as gold:
Her skin was as white as leprosy,
The Nightmare Life-in-Death was she,
Who thicks man's blood with cold.

The naked hulk alongside came,

Death and Life-in-Death have diced for the ship's crew, and she (the latter) winneth the ancient Mariner.

And the twain were casting dice;
"The game is done! I've won! I've won!"
Quoth she, and whistles thrice.

The Sun's rim dips; the stars rush out:

No twilight within the courts of the Sun.

At one stride comes the dark;
With far-heard whisper, o'er the sea,
Off shot the spectre-bark.

157

We listen'd and look'd sideways up
Fear at my heart, as at a cup,
My life-blood seem'd to sip!
The stars were dim, and thick the night,
The steersman's face by his lamp gleam'd white;

From the sails the dew did drip—
Till clomb above the eastern bar
The hornèd Moon, with one bright star
Within the nether tip.

At the rising
the Moon.

One after one, by the star-dogg'd Moon,
Too quick for groan or sigh,
Each turn'd his face with a ghastly pang,
And cursed me with his eye.

One after another.

Four times fifty living men
(And I heard nor sigh nor groan),
With heavy thump, a lifeless lump,
They dropp'd down one by one.

His shipmates drop
down dead.

The souls did from their bodies fly—
They fled to bliss or woe!
And every soul, it pass'd me by
Like the whizz of my crossbow!'

But Life-in-Death
begins her work
on the ancient
Mariner.

PART IV

'I fear thee, ancient Mariner!
I fear thy skinny hand!
And thou art long, and lank, and brown,
As is the ribb'd sea-sand.

The Wedding-
Guest feareth that
a spirit is talking
to him.

I fear thee and thy glittering eye,
And thy skinny hand so brown.'—
'Fear not, fear not, thou Wedding-Guest!
This body dropt not down.

But the ancient
Mariner assureth
him of his bodily
life, and pro-
ceedeth to relate
his horrible
penance.

Alone, alone, all, all alone,
Alone on a wide, wide sea!
And never a saint took pity on
My soul in agony.

The many men, so beautiful!
And they all dead did lie:
And a thousand thousand slimy things
Lived on; and so did I.

He despiseth the
creatures of the
calm.

I look'd upon the rotting sea,
And drew my eyes away;
I look'd upon the rotting deck,
And there the dead men lay.

And envieth that
they should live,
and so many lie
dead.

I look'd to heaven, and tried to pray;
But or ever a prayer had gusht,
A wicked whisper came, and made
My heart as dry as dust.

I closed my lids, and kept them close,
And the balls like pulses beat;
For the sky and the sea, and the sea and the sky,
Lay like a load on my weary eye,
And the dead were at my feet.

The cold sweat melted from their limbs,
Nor rot nor reek did they:
The look with which they look'd on me
Had never pass'd away.

But the curse
liveth for him in
the eye of the
dead men.

An orphan's curse would drag to hell
A spirit from on high;
But oh! more horrible than that
Is the curse in a dead man's eye!
Seven days, seven nights, I saw that curse,
And yet I could not die.

The moving Moon went up the sky,
And nowhere did abide;
Softly she was going up,
And a star or two beside—

In his loneliness
and fixedness he
yearneth towards
the journeying
Moon, and the
stars that still
sojourn, yet still
move onward;
and everywhere
the blue sky be-
longs to them, and
is their appointed
rest and their
native country and
their own natural
homes, which
they enter un-
announced, as
lords that are cer-
tainly expected,
and yet there is a
silent joy at their
arrival.

Her beams bemock'd the sultry main,
Like April hoar-frost spread;
But where the ship's huge shadow lay,
The charmèd water burnt alway
A still and awful red.

By the light of the
Moon he be-
holdeth God's
creatures of the
great calm.

Beyond the shadow of the ship,
I watch'd the water-snakes:
They moved in tracks of shining white,
And when they rear'd, the elfish light
Fell off in hoary flakes.

160

Within the shadow of the ship
I watch'd their rich attire:
Blue, glossy green, and velvet black,
They coil'd and swam; and every track
Was a flash of golden fire.

O happy living things! no tongue
Their beauty might declare:
A spring of love gush'd from my heart,
And I bless'd them unaware:
Sure my kind saint took pity on me,
And I bless'd them unaware.

Their beauty and
their happiness.

He blesseth them
in his heart.

The self-same moment I could pray;
And from my neck so free
The Albatross fell off, and sank
Like lead into the sea.

The Spell begin
to break.

PART V

'O sleep! it is a gentle thing,
Beloved from pole to pole!
To Mary Queen the praise be given!
She sent the gentle sleep from Heaven,
That slid into my soul.

The silly[1] buckets on the deck,
That had so long remain'd,
I dreamt that they were fill'd with dew;
And when I awoke, it rain'd.

By grace of the
holy Mother, the
ancient Mariner
refreshed with
rain.

Useless.

161

My lips were wet, my throat was cold,
My garments all were dank;
Sure I had drunken in my dreams,
And still my body drank.

I moved, and could not feel my limbs:
I was so light—almost
I thought that I had died in sleep,
And was a blessèd ghost.

And soon I heard a roaring wind:
It did not come anear;
But with its sound it shook the sails,
That were so thin and sere.

He heareth sounds
and seeth strange
sights and com-
motions in the sky
and the element.

The upper air burst into life!
And a hundred fire-flags sheen,
To and fro they were hurried about!
And to and fro, and in and out,
The wan stars danced between.

And the coming wind did roar more loud,
And the sails did sigh like sedge;
And the rain pour'd down from one black cloud;
The Moon was at its edge.

The thick black cloud was cleft, and still
The Moon was at its side;
Like waters shot from some high crag,
The lightning fell with never a jag,
A river steep and wide.

The loud wind never reach'd the ship,
Yet now the ship moved on!
Beneath the lightning and the Moon
The dead men gave a groan.

The bodies of
the ship's crew
are inspired, and
the ship moves on;

They groan'd, they stirr'd, they all uprose,
Nor spake, nor moved their eyes;
It had been strange, even in a dream,
To have seen those dead men rise.

The helmsman steer'd, the ship moved on;
Yet never a breeze up-blew;
The mariners all 'gan work the ropes,
Where they were wont to do;
They raised their limbs like lifeless tools—
We were a ghastly crew.

The body of my brother's son
Stood by me, knee to knee:
The body and I pull'd at one rope,
But he said naught to me.'

'I fear thee, ancient Mariner!'
'Be calm, thou Wedding-Guest:
'Twas not those souls that fled in pain,
Which to their corses came again,
But a troop of spirits blest:

But not by the
souls of the men,
nor by demons of
earth or middle
air, but by a
blessed troop of
angelic spirits,
sent down by the
invocation of the
guardian saint.

For when it dawn'd—they dropp'd their arms,
And cluster'd round the mast;
Sweet sounds rose slowly through their mouths,
And from their bodies pass'd.

Around, around, flew each sweet sound,
Then darted to the Sun;
Slowly the sounds came back again,
Now mix'd, now one by one.

Sometimes a-dropping from the sky
I heard the skylark sing;
Sometimes all little birds that are,
How they seem'd to fill the sea and air
With their sweet jargoning!

And now 'twas like all instruments,
Now like a lonely flute;
And now it is an angel's song,
That makes the Heavens be mute.

It ceased; yet still the sails made on
A pleasant noise till noon,
A noise like of a hidden brook
In the leafy month of June,
That to the sleeping woods all night
Singeth a quiet tune.

Till noon we quietly sail'd on,
Yet never a breeze did breathe:
Slowly and smoothly went the ship,
Moved onward from beneath.

Under the keel nine fathom deep,
From the land of mist and snow,
The Spirit slid: and it was he
That made the ship to go.
The sails at noon left off their tune,
And the ship stood still also.

The Sun, right up above the mast,
Had fix'd her to the ocean:
But in a minute she 'gan stir,
With a short uneasy motion—
Backwards and forwards half her length
With a short uneasy motion.

Then like a pawing horse let go,
She made a sudden bound;
It flung the blood into my head,
And I fell down in a swound.

How long in that same fit I lay,
I have not to declare;
But ere my living life return'd,
I heard, and in my soul discern'd
Two voices in the air.

"Is it he?" quoth one, "is this the man?
By Him who died on cross,
With his cruel bow he laid full low
The harmless Albatross.

SAMUEL TAYLOR COLERIDGE (1772–1834)
from a crayon drawing by an unknown artist

The Spirit who bideth by himself
In the land of mist and snow,
He loved the bird that loved the man
Who shot him with his bow."

The other was a softer voice,
As soft as honey-dew:
Quoth he, "The man hath penance done,
And penance more will do."

PART VI

First Voice:
"But tell me, tell me! speak again,
Thy soft response renewing—
What makes that ship drive on so fast?
What is the Ocean doing?"

Second Voice:
"Still as a slave before his lord,
The Ocean hath no blast;
His great bright eye most silently
Up to the Moon is cast—

If he may know which way to go;
For she guides him smooth or grim.
See, brother, see! how graciously
She looketh down on him."

First Voice:

"But why drives on that ship so fast,
Without or wave or wind?"

Second Voice:

"The air is cut away before,
And closes from behind.

Fly, brother, fly! more high, more high!
Or we shall be belated:
For slow and slow that ship will go,
When the Mariner's trance is abated."

I woke, and we were sailing on
As in a gentle weather:
'Twas night, calm night, the Moon was high;
The dead men stood together.

All stood together on the deck,
For a charnel-dungeon fitter:
All fix'd on me their stony eyes,
That in the Moon did glitter.

The pang, the curse, with which they died,
Had never pass'd away:
I could not draw my eyes from theirs,
Nor turn them up to pray.

And now this spell was snapt: once more
I viewed the ocean green,
And look'd far forth, yet little saw
Of what had else been seen—

The Mariner hath been cast into a trance; for the angelic power causeth the vessel to drive northward faster than human life could endure.

The supernatural motion is retarded; the Mariner awakes, and his penance begins anew.

The curse is finally expiated.

Like one that on a lonesome road
Doth walk in fear and dread,
And having once turn'd round, walks on,
And turns no more his head;
Because he knows a frightful fiend
Doth close behind him tread.

But soon there breathed a wind on me,
Nor sound nor motion made:
Its path was not upon the sea,
In ripple or in shade.

It raised my hair, it fann'd my cheek
Like a meadow-gale of spring—
It mingled strangely with my fears,
Yet it felt like a welcoming.

Swiftly, swiftly flew the ship,
Yet she sail'd softly too:
Sweetly, sweetly blew the breeze—
On me alone it blew.

O dream of joy! is this indeed
The lighthouse top I see?
Is this the hill? is this the kirk?
Is this mine own countree?

And the ancient
Mariner beholdeth
his native country.

We drifted o'er the harbour-bar,
And I with sobs did pray—
O let me be awake, my God!
Or let me sleep alway.

The harbour-bay was clear as glass,
So smoothly it was strewn!
And on the bay the moonlight lay,
And the shadow of the Moon.

The rock shone bright, the kirk no less
That stands above the rock:
The moonlight steep'd in silentness
The steady weathercock.

And the bay was white with silent light, *The angelic spirits*
Till rising from the same, *leave the dead*
Full many shapes, that shadows were, *bodies*
In crimson colours came.

A little distance from the prow *And appear in*
Those crimson shadows were: *their own forms*
I turn'd my eyes upon the deck— *of light.*
O Christ! what saw I there!

Each corse lay flat, lifeless and flat,
And, by the holy rood!
A man all light, a seraph-man,
On every corse there stood.

This seraph-band, each waved his hand:
It was a heavenly sight!
They stood as signals to the land,
Each one a lovely light;

This seraph-band, each waved his hand:
No voice did they impart—
No voice; but O, the silence sank
Like music on my heart.

But soon I heard the dash of oars,
I heard the Pilot's cheer;
My head was turn'd perforce away,
And I saw a boat appear.

The Pilot and the Pilot's boy,
I heard them coming fast:
Dear Lord in Heaven! it was a joy
The dead men could not blast.

I saw a third—I heard his voice:
It is the Hermit good!
He singeth loud his godly hymns
That he makes in the wood.
He'll shrieve my soul, he'll wash away
The Albatross's blood.

Part VII

'This Hermit good lives in that wood
Which slopes down to the sea.
How loudly his sweet voice he rears!
He loves to talk with marineres
That come from a far countree.

The Hermit of the
Wood.

He kneels at morn, and noon, and eve—
He hath a cushion plump:
It is the moss that wholly hides
The rotted old oak-stump.

The skiff-boat near'd: I heard them talk,
"Why, this is strange, I trow!
Where are those lights so many and fair,
That signal made but now?"

"Strange, by my faith!" the Hermit said— *Approacheth the ship with wonder*
"And they answer'd not our cheer!
The planks look warp'd! and see those sails,
How thin they are and sere!
I never saw aught like to them,
Unless perchance it were

Brown skeletons of leaves that lag
My forest-brook along;
When the ivy-tod is heavy with snow,
And the owlet whoops to the wolf below,
That eats the she-wolf's young."

"Dear Lord! it hath a fiendish look—
(The Pilot made reply)
I am a-fear'd."—"Push on, push on!"
Said the Hermit cheerily.

The boat came closer to the ship,
But I nor spake nor stirr'd;
The boat came close beneath the ship,
And straight a sound was heard.

172

Under the water it rumbled on,
Still louder and more dread:
It reach'd the ship, it split the bay;
The ship went down like lead.

The ship suddenly
sinketh.

Stunn'd by that loud and dreadful sound,
Which sky and ocean smote,
Like one that hath been seven days drown'd
My body lay afloat;
But swift as dreams, myself I found
Within the Pilot's boat.

The ancient
Mariner is saved
in the Pilot's boat.

Upon the whirl, where sank the ship
The boat spun round and round;
And all was still, save that the hill
Was telling of the sound.

I moved my lips—the Pilot shriek'd
And fell down in a fit;
The holy Hermit raised his eyes,
And pray'd where he did sit.

I took the oars: the Pilot's boy,
Who now doth crazy go,
Laugh'd loud and long, and all the while
His eyes went to and fro.
"Ha! ha!" quoth he, "full plain I see
The Devil knows how to row."

And now, all in my own countree,
I stood on the firm land!
The Hermit stepp'd forth from the boat,
And scarcely could he stand.

173

"O shrieve me, shrieve me, holy man!"
The Hermit cross'd his brow.
"Say quick," quoth he, "I bid thee say—
What manner of man art thou?"

The ancient Mariner earnestly entreateth the Hermit to shrieve him; and the penance of life falls on him.

Forthwith this frame of mine was wrench'd
With a woeful agony,
Which forced me to begin my tale;
And then it left me free.

Since then, at an uncertain hour,
That agony returns:
And till my ghastly tale is told,
This heart within me burns.

And ever and anon throughout his future life an agony constraineth him to travel from land to land;

I pass, like night, from land to land;
I have strange power of speech;
That moment that his face I see,
I know the man that must hear me:
To him my tale I teach.

What loud uproar bursts from that door!
The wedding-guests are there:
But in the garden-bower the bride
And bride-maids singing are:
And hark the little vesper bell,
Which biddeth me to prayer!

O Wedding-Guest! this soul hath been
Alone on a wide, wide sea:
So lonely 'twas, that God himself
Scarce seemèd there to be.

O sweeter than the marriage-feast,
'Tis sweeter far to me,
To walk together to the kirk
With a goodly company!—

To walk together to the kirk,
And all together pray,
While each to his great Father bends,
Old men, and babes, and loving friends,
And youths and maidens gay!

Farewell, farewell! but this I tell
To thee, thou Wedding-Guest!
He prayeth well, who loveth well
Both man and bird and beast.

And to teach, by his own example, love and reverence to all things that God made and loveth.

He prayeth best, who loveth best
All things both great and small;
For the dear God who loveth us,
He made and loveth all.'

The Mariner, whose eye is bright,
Whose beard with age is hoar,
Is gone: and now the Wedding-Guest
Turn'd from the bridegroom's door.

He went like one that hath been stunn'd,
And is of sense forlorn:
A sadder and a wiser man
He rose the morrow morn.

SAMUEL TAYLOR COLERIDGE

175

ACKNOWLEDGEMENTS

THE EDITOR and publishers wish to thank the following for their permission to include copyright material in this anthology: Mr Edmund Blunden for 'Winter: East Anglia'; Mrs H. M. Davies and Messrs Jonathan Cape Ltd for 'The Bust' and 'The Sailor to His Parrot' from *The Collected Poems of W. H. Davies*; Messrs Jonathan Cape Ltd for 'In Hardwood Groves', 'The Runaway' and 'Stopping by Woods on a Snowy Evening' from *The Complete Poems of Robert Frost*, and 'Last Snow' and 'Wiltshire Downs' from *The Collected Poems of Andrew Young*; The Society of Authors and Messrs Jonathan Cape Ltd for 'The Carpenter's Son' and 'The Street Sounds to the Soldiers' Tread' by A. E. Housman; Messrs Chatto & Windus Ltd for 'Miners' by Wilfred Owen; the Literary Trustees of Walter de la Mare and Messrs Faber & Faber for 'The Listeners'; Messrs Faber & Faber for 'Prelude: The winter evening settles down' and 'The Unemployed' from *The Rock*, both from *Collected Poems of T. S. Eliot*; Mr Robert Graves for 'The "General Elliott"' and '1805' from *The Collected Poems of Robert Graves* published by Messrs Cassell & Co.; Messrs Constable & Co. Ltd for three poems by Arthur Waley and 'The Artist' by Sir Walter Raleigh; the Trustees of the Hardy Estate and Messrs Macmillan & Co. Ltd for four poems by Thomas Hardy; the Estate of the late Mrs Frieda Lawrence for four poems by D. H. Lawrence; Mrs Flecker for 'The Old Ships' by J. E. Flecker; Mrs Stephens and Messrs Macmillan & Co. Ltd for 'The Main-Deep' and 'O Bruadair' from *Collected Poems* by James Stephens; the Macmillan Company, New York, for 'The Daniel Jazz' by Vachel Lindsay; Mr Siegfried Sassoon for 'Morning Express' and 'The General'; the Clarendon Press, Oxford, for 'The Whale' and 'Riddle on Moon and Sun' by Gavin Bone from *Anglo-Saxon Poetry*, and the Oxford University Press for 'Poor Rumble' from *The Blackbird in the Lilac* by James Reeves. The Authorized Version of the Holy Bible is Crown copyright, and the two extracts from it are here reproduced by permission. Thanks are also due to the U.S. Information Services for the illustration on page 26, to the Fitzwilliam Museum, Cambridge, for the portrait on page 73, to the Trustees of the British Museum for the illustrations on pages 42 and 110, to the Trustees of the National Portrait Gallery for the portrait on page 118, and to Mrs C. S. Gardner for the portrait on page 166.

INDEX OF TITLES AND FIRST LINES

Titles are given in italic type

INDEX OF AUTHORS